Other Titles of Interest

AN INTRODUCTION TO
AMATEUR RADIO

by

I. D. POOLE
B.Sc.(Eng.), C.Eng., M.I.E.E., G3YWX

**BERNARD BABANI (publishing) LTD
THE GRAMPIANS
SHEPHERDS BUSH ROAD
LONDON W6 7NF
ENGLAND**

Please Note

Although every care has been taken with the production of this
book to ensure that any projects, designs, modifications and/or
programs, etc., contained herewith, operate in a correct and safe
manner and also that any components specified are normally
available in Great Britain, the Publishers do not accept responsibility in any way for the failure, including fault in design, of
any project, design, modification or program to work correctly
or to cause damage to any other equipment that it may be
connected to or used in conjunction with, or in respect of any
other damage or injury that may be so caused, nor do the
Publishers accept responsibility in any way for the failure to
obtain specified components.

Notice is also given that if equipment that is still under
warranty is modified in any way or used or connected with
home-built equipment then that warranty may be void.

First Published – August 1989
Reprinted – December 1992
Revised and Reprinted – April 1998

British Library Cataloguing in Publication Data

Poole, I. D.

An introduction to amateur radio

1. Amateur radio communication

I. Title

621.3841'66

ISBN 0 85934 202 6

Cover Design by Gregor Arthur

Printed and bound in Great Britain by Cox & Wyman Ltd, Reading

Contents

Chapter 1

WHAT IS AMATEUR RADIO?

Amateur radio is a fascinating hobby which has captivated the interest of many thousands of people since its foundation at the beginning of the twentieth century. It can be a relaxing hobby, as well as being creative and useful. In fact many people have made friends all over the world and enjoy talking to them regularly over the air. Some people have taken a great interest in the technical side of the hobby and gone on to make their hobby into a career they enjoy. The hobby can also benefit the community as a whole. This can be particularly seen in times of disaster when radio amateurs can use their equipment and expertise to help the emergency services.

People's interests will vary widely. Some will enjoy operating most of all, whilst others will prefer the constructional side. In fact each person will have his own particular brand of amateur radio. But whatever one's preference, there will always be plenty to keep a healthy interest alive in the hobby.

The Development of Amateur Radio in the U.K.

The foundation of amateur radio dates back to the discoveries made at the end of nineteenth century by famous names like Hertz, Maxwell and Edison. These people made the original discoveries which were later developed and improved by other people.

One such person was Guglielmo Marconi, an Italian born man who came to England in 1896 after his ideas were rejected in his homeland. It was Marconi who first made wireless a useable and commercial proposition. He was the first person to send a wireless signal over water, and he also made many developments in the receiving and transmitting apparatus of the day. Later he went on to transmit signals over the Channel and then he was the first person to send a signal across the Atlantic.

At this time it was possible for anyone to use a transmitter in the U.K. but in 1905 it became necessary to obtain a licence.

These licences were issued for the purposes of experimentation and were the forerunner of today's amateur licences. They were very popular and within the first year just under a hundred were issued to a wide variety of people. One noteable name in the list was Dr J. A. Fleming of University College London who was the inventor of the diode valve as well as being a consultant to Marconi and the designer of the transmitter which first spanned the Atlantic.

These experimental licences were issued up until the onset of war in 1914. At this time all licences were revoked and all wireless equipment, including transmitters as well as receivers, was impounded. It was also made an offence to possess any wireless equipment and anyone found with any was liable to imprisonment.

After the war licences were not issued until 1920. Again, they were called experimental licences and not amateur ones. In order to obtain a licence it was necessary to outline a set of experiments for which a licence was required. In addition to this it now became necessary to pass a theory examination as well as a Morse Code test. Operation was also restricted to the shorter wavelengths which were thought to be of little use at that time.

Despite these extra requirements many licences were issued and amateur radio developed rapidly. Initially communication had only been possible over short distances, but after a short while contacts were made between different countries. Then in December 1921 the first signals were heard across the Atlantic and later in November 1923 the first two-way contact was made. By doing this radio amateurs had proved that the short wave bands were useful after all.

Technology progressed rapidly in these years and great advances were made in many areas of radio. Not only did the design of the equipment improve, but so did the understanding of topics like the propagation of radio waves. Much of this was as a direct result of the work done by radio amateurs.

War broke out again in 1939 and with it all amateur operations ceased. Licences were revoked and all transmitting equipment was impounded for the duration of the war. In spite of this many amateur radio publications continued and were of great use and interest to those serving in the forces.

In addition to this a large number of radio amateurs were able to use their operating skill and technical knowledge in vital roles towards the war effort.

After the war finished a new type of licence was proposed. This was a true amateur licence which removed many of the petty restrictions which had previously been imposed on the amateur experimenters.

It also gave many more facilities in line with other countries. The requirements for obtaining a licence were also rationalised. It now only became necessary to pass a theory examination and a Morse test. It was also agreed that holders of pre-war licences would be reissued with their old callsigns without the need for retaking either the theory examination or the Morse test. Finally these new licences started to be issued at the beginning of 1946 and amateur radio began to flourish again.

As time passed the licence conditions were changed to allow amateurs more freedom and flexibility. In 1954 new licences were issued which enabled amateurs to use transmitting equipment in their cars. Reflecting the advance in technology another type of licence was introduced in the same year allowing amateurs to transmit television. Then, ten years later, another type of licence was introduced which only allowed operation on frequencies above 430 MHz, but it could be obtained without passing the Morse test. Two years later the terms of this licence were expanded to allow the use of two metre operation.

Since then there have been further facilities added to the licence. New bands have been introduced, the requirements for a separate mobile or television licence have been removed, and the licence conditions relaxed to enable amateurs more freedom on the air. There have also been a large number of technological advances. For example, there is an extensive network of repeaters in use on the VHF and UHF bands, amateur satellite operation is fairly commonplace and new types of error resilient data transmission are available. All of these advances and many, many more give an indication of the forward looking nature and inventiveness of the hobby of amateur radio as it is today.

Aspects of Amateur Radio

Amateur radio encompasses a very wide range of interests and activities. Some people will be more interested in certain parts of the hobby than others. In fact, each person will have his own brand of the hobby as it is possible to choose what aspects of the hobby to follow.

Many people start their interest in amateur radio by becoming a short wave listener. In order to listen on the bands, all that is required is a communications receiver, an aerial and away you go. It is an ideal introduction to the hobby because it is possible to learn a lot. Not only is it possible to find out about topics like the nature of propagation from first-hand experience, but it is also possible to learn a lot from simply listening to others talking about the hobby.

Having been a listener for a while many people will want to go on and obtain a transmitting licence. In order to obtain one it is necessary to pass a theory examination for a class B licence. If a class A licence is to be obtained allowing access to all the amateur bands a Morse test also has to be passed. Once the licence has been obtained some people enjoy chatting to friends across town or at the other side of the world. Others enjoy DXing. This is a term referring to long distance contacts, but it has also come to mean contacting stations in rare or little heard countries.

There are other sidelines associated with DXing. Often people send QSL cards to confirm a contact. In their basic form these cards just have the details of a contact written on them as a confirmation that the contact took place. However, many stations have very attractive cards printed which can be used to decorate the walls of the radio shack. Of course, they are even better if they are from a station in a rare or little heard country far away.

In addition to collecting QSL cards some people also collect operating awards. These awards can present new operating challenges, as well as looking very attractive if they are mounted on the wall. There is a great variety of awards available, but one of the most famous is DXCC. The letters stand for DX Century Club, and it is given by the ARRL (The American Radio Relay League — the American national radio society) to people who can prove they have made contact with

4

a hundred countries. Once the basic award has been obtained endorsement stickers can be added as more countries are contacted.

Although operating the equipment forms a large part of amateur radio, many people enjoy constructing their own equipment. Whilst some people will build all their own equipment many more will buy the large, more complicated items and set about building many of the other pieces of gear needed around the station. Building some of one's own equipment gives a great sense of satisfaction and increases one's pride in the station.

Another area where the amateur becomes very involved is in erecting an aerial system. As the performance of the aerial will determine the overall effectiveness of the station it is vital that it operates well. As a result of this many people find great satisfaction and interest in experimenting with aerials and trying to make them operate as well and efficiently as possible.

Apart from the bias to either operating or construction, there are also choices to be made about which bands are favoured. Some people enjoy the HF bands below 30 MHz with the possibility of plenty of long distance contacts. Other people will prefer the challenge of operating or building equipment for the VHF and UHF bands. In addition to this there is also a rapidly growing number of people who are interested in the microwave bands and the possibilities of breaking new barriers on higher and higher frequencies.

These are only a few of the various areas of interest in amateur radio. The variety which is given has the advantage that people remain interested and engrossed for a lifetime.

Chapter 2

TYPES OF TRANSMISSION

Having located an amateur band on a receiver it is highly likely that there will be all manner of peculiar noises there, and few, if any, of them will be intelligible. It may be possible to detect morse signals, other types of keyed signals, noises which sound as though they may have been speech at one time but are certainly not intelligible now, and a whole host of other signals. In fact it would be very surprising if any signals could be made to yield intelligible sound if a domestic radio with a short wave band was used.

The reason for using all these different types of transmission is that they are all communicating in different ways. Each type of signal has its own characteristics and advantages. Some signals are obviously morse and can be copied if the code is known. Other signals are different types of data transmission. These days home computers are often linked into the transmitter and receiver to generate or decode the data and display it on a screen. Then the signals which sound like garbled speech are a form of voice communication. The signal has been generated in such a way that it makes the best use of the available power and spectrum. Because of this extra electronic circuitry is required in the receiver for it to be copied.

In order to know what the transmissions consist of and how to decode them a little more explanation is required.

Morse

Morse is the simplest and yet one of the most effective forms of modulating or encoding information onto a radio signal. In fact it was the first method which was used and in spite of the tremendous developments which have taken place in radio it is still used under many circumstances. This is because it still possesses several distinct advantages over other modes even in today's "high tech" environment.

Probably one of the most obvious advantages is that morse, or CW as it is sometimes called, can be transmitted using

7

comparatively simple equipment. All that is needed is an RF oscillator to generate the signal or carrier as illustrated in Figure 2.1, an amplifier with matching circuitry to bring it to

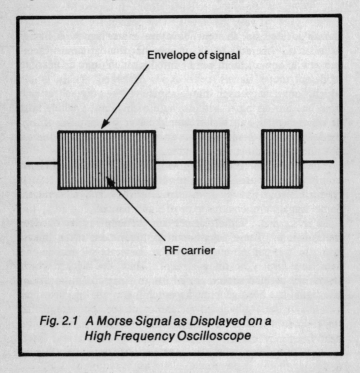

**Fig. 2.1 A Morse Signal as Displayed on a
High Frequency Oscilloscope**

the required level and deliver it to the aerial and finally a method of turning the signal on and off with a morse key. This can be done by using as few as two transistors, although more often than not more complicated higher power and more versatile transmitters are used. Even so, this is of particular interest to radio amateurs because it means that it is possible to contact stations all over the world using equipment which is very simple by today's standards. It also means that the equipment for CW is very much easier to build and projects like these can be undertaken by the average radio amateur without too much difficulty.

Apart from the simplicity of the equipment there are several technical advantages. Because of the simplicity of a morse signal — it only consists of turning a signal on and off and the rate of signalling is fairly slow — it is possible to copy morse signals at very low levels. One reason for this is that it is very much easier to copy a low level morse signal which just requires the operator to detect whether the carrier is present or not. A complicated speech signal is much more difficult to read.

The other reason is that a morse signal only takes up a small amount of bandwidth because of its slow signalling rate. This means that much narrower receiver bandwidths can be used and this will obviously reduce the amount of noise and the number of interfering signals. For example, it is quite possible to use a receiver bandwidth of as little as 500 Hz or even 250 Hz when copying morse. Other forms of speech transmission may require bandwidths of 2.5 KHz or more depending upon the actual type of transmission.

In order that a radio receiver can properly resolve a morse signal it needs some extra circuitry. Unfortunately a normal domestic radio will not produce the characteristic audio tone associated with a morse signal. For this to be achieved a "beat frequency oscillator" is required in most cases. This is just an oscillator which beats with the incoming morse signal to give an audio tone. In fact the frequency of the tone is equal to the frequency difference between the incoming signal and the beat frequency oscillator. This is usually done at the intermediate frequency within the receiver as explained in Chapter 6.

Amplitude Modulation
Even though morse possesses many advantages it still cannot replace the spoken word, and it cannot be used to transmit entertainment. In order to be able to transmit music and speech the radio signal has to be modulated by the sounds in one way or another. There are several ways in which this can be done, but the most obvious is to modulate the amplitude of the signal.

Amplitude modulation, or AM for short, is the mode which is used by broadcast stations on the long, medium and short

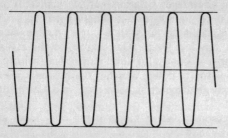

a) A radio frequency carrier

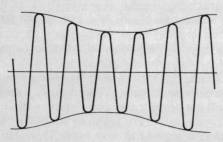

b) The carrier with some amplitude modulation

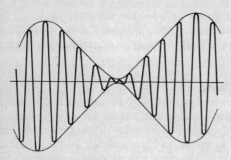

Twice the level when modulation is applied

c) 100% modulation

Fig 2.2 Amplitude Modulation of an RF Carrier

wave bands. Its main advantage is in its simplicity, particularly in the receiver which only needs a simple diode detector. Unfortunately AM is very inefficient in its use of power and bandwidth. This has meant that it is only rarely used for communications purposes these days, and accordingly radio amateurs are seldom heard using it.

In order to understand why it is not very efficient it is necessary to look at a bit of background theory. Figure 2.2(a) shows an unmodulated RF carrier. If it then has modulation applied to it the envelope will vary as shown in Figure 2.2(b). However it can be seen that there is still room to apply some more modulation. In fact the maximum amount which can be applied occurs when the envelope falls to zero and rises to twice the original level, as shown in Figure 2.2(c). When this level is reached the carrier is said to have 100% modulation.

Even when the carrier has 100% modulation the utilisation of the power is still poor. To investigate this further it is necessary to look at what happens to the frequency spectrum when the carrier is modulated. So that matters are simplified let us say that the modulating signal is just a 1 KHz tone — the same arguments are true for speech or music, but the diagram becomes less complicated.

Figure 2.3(a) shows a carrier. When it is modulated by the 1 KHz tone it is found that there are two sidebands either side of the carrier and 1 KHz away from it. The voltage level of the sidebands varies and is dependent upon the amount of modulation which is present. When the carrier is fully modulated they rise to 50% of the level of the carrier. In fact in terms of power the picture is even less attractive as each sideband is only a quarter of the level of the carrier, i.e., a 100 watt carrier when fully modulated will have two sidebands of only 25 watts each.

Whilst a signal is being modulated like this the carrier remains constant in level and only acts as a reference for demodulating the signal in the receiver. It is the sidebands which actually carry the useful information. From this it can be seen that it is only a small proportion of the signal power which carries the useful information and this is why AM is very wasteful from the point of view of power.

11

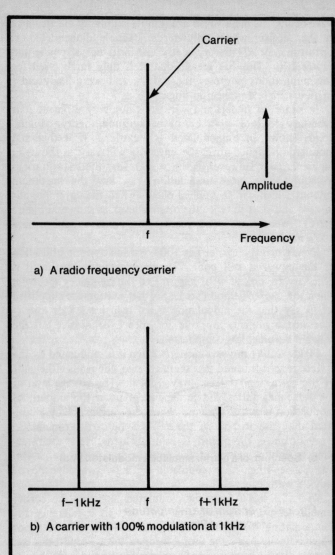

a) A radio frequency carrier

b) A carrier with 100% modulation at 1kHz

Fig. 2.3 The Spectrum of a Carrier Modulated by a 1kHz Tone

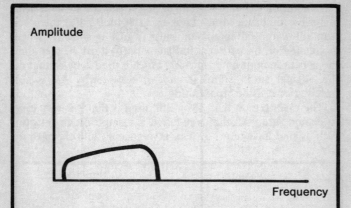

a) Spectrum of a typical audio signal

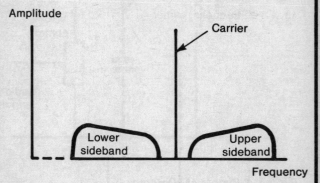

b) Spectrum of a carrier amplitude modulated by a)

Fig. 2.4 Spectrum of an Amplitude Modulated Signal

13

In addition to being wasteful of power AM is also inefficient in its use of bandwidth. Looking at Figure 2.4(a) the spectrum of a typical speech or music signal is shown. When modulated onto a carrier as in Figure 2.4(b) it can be seen that the actual amount of bandwidth which is used is twice that of the original audio. This is another reason why AM is not widely used outside broadcasting.

The main reason that AM is still used is that it is very easy to demodulate. All that is required is a simple diode detector such as that in Figure 2.5. This is very simple and cheap to fit

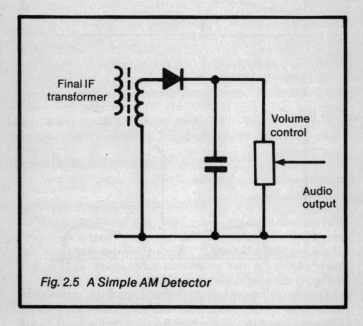

Fig. 2.5   A Simple AM Detector

into receivers, and it makes AM the ideal mode for use with mass produced receivers where cost is a prime consideration.

Single Sideband

Single sideband or SSB as it is called is the most commonly used mode for long distance speech communication. When received on a receiver with just an envelope detector used for

AM it sounds very garbled and totally incomprehensible. This hides its advantages which make it the most efficient form of voice communication, particularly in poor conditions.

Essentially SSB is a derivative of AM. It is basically an AM signal with the unwanted parts removed to leave only those which contribute to carrying the speech or sounds themselves.

One of the disadvantages of AM was that it possessed a large carrier which did not contribute anything to the signal except in providing a reference to be used during demodulation. As the reference can be provided in the receiver with a little extra circuitry there is even less point in keeping it. In fact the carrier can be easily removed in the transmitter either by filters, or special mixers (balanced or double balanced mixers) or a combination of the two. This leaves a signal containing just the two sidebands but no carrier.

The other disadvantage of AM was that it occupied a bandwidth which was twice that of the audio it carried. As both sidebands carry what is essentially the same signal (one is the exact mirror image of the other) and it is difficult to resolve a signal using both the sidebands and no carrier it seems logical to remove one. This is usually done using a filter, but there are other ways using phasing techniques. Having done this a signal containing one sideband with no carrier remains, and this is what SSB is.

As both sidebands are identical in every respect except that they are mirror images of each other, it is possible to use either one. However, it makes matters very much easier if some form of convention is adopted. Almost without exception the lower sideband is used on amateur bands below 10 MHz, and the upper sideband is used above 10 MHz.

In order to resolve a single sideband signal it is necessary to reinsert the carrier. This is done in the receiver using a beat frequency oscillator, or a carrier insertion oscillator. Both are in fact one and the same despite the different names. Once the carrier has been inserted and the signal detected the original audio is obtained.

The main problem with SSB is that it is necessary to reinsert the carrier at the correct frequency. For amateur communications it is possible to tolerate an offset of a 100 Hz or more. Any frequency offset will raise or lower the pitch of the voice giving it a rather peculiar "tone". This will still leave it quite intelligible unless the frequency offset is too great. However for some applications it is necessary to reinsert the carrier on exactly the right frequency. This can be done if the carrier is not completely suppressed in the transmitter. Using some extra circuitry in the receiver it is possible to lock the carrier insertion oscillator onto exactly the right frequency. In this way it is possible to regenerate the audio exactly as it was transmitted.

Frequency Modulation
Modulating the amplitude of an RF signal is the most obvious way of applying audio to an RF signal. Even so it is by no means the only way. There are several other methods each of which has its own advantages. One of these other methods is frequency modulation.

As the name implies, frequency modulation involves changing the frequency of a signal according to the changes in level of the modulating signal. Looking at Figure 2.6 it can be seen that the frequency of the signal increases as the voltage of the modulating signal increases and conversely decreases as the voltage falls.

The amount the frequency changes is called the deviation. This can be made to be fairly small (about 3 KHz) for narrow band frequency modulation (NBFM) or much wider (possibly around 75 KHz) for wide band FM. In order to be able to define the level of modulation a modulation index is used. This is defined as the actual amount of deviation divided by the modulating frequency.

FM finds its uses mainly in the VHF and higher sections of the spectrum. It is probably best known for its use in the high quality wideband FM broadcast transmissions between 88 and 108 MHz. However as narrowband FM it also finds widespread use for mobile and other radio applications, in both commercial and amateur use.

Its main advantage is its immunity to noise. As all the modulation is carried in the variations of frequency, the receiver can be made quite immune to any amplitude variations. It is found that most of the received noise will be amplitude noise, so once the signal has reached a certain level

16

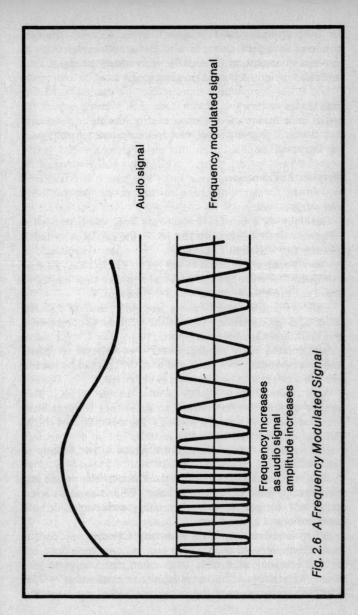

Audio signal

Frequency modulated signal

Frequency increases
as audio signal
amplitude increases

Fig. 2.6 A Frequency Modulated Signal

the level of background noise will be quite low. Another advantage is that fading can also be unnoticeable. This is particularly important for mobile radio where the signal level fluctuates rapidly as the vehicle is moving.

Data Modes

Apart from morse and speech it is also possible to send data over the air. This is a mode of communication which is gaining increased popularity as modern technology has had a great impact in this area. Originally bulky mechanical teletypes or teleprinters were used, but now it is possible to use much smaller printers with the possibility of using computers as well.

Generally data communications use FSK which stands for Frequency Shift Keying. In this mode the carrier is switched between two different frequencies. The system is operated in this way because it is much easier for an electronic system to distinguish between two defined states rather than having to detect the presence or absence of a signal as in CW.

FSK systems generally have a frequency shift of 175 Hz, i.e., ± 87.5 Hz deviation. One of the frequencies corresponds to a mark and the other corresponds to a space. The RF signal is demodulated in the receiver so that two voltages are generated corresponding to a mark and a space. This can be used to generate a teleprinter or computer as necessary.

Apart from FSK it is also possible to use AFSK. This consists of a carrier onto which an audio tone is modulated. The tone has its frequency shifted. The advantage of this is that the receiver tuning is less critical, but it does require more bandwidth. As a result of this AFSK is used mainly at VHF and above.

A variety of data rates are used. The old teleprinters and teletypes operated at 45.5 or 50 baud (1 baud usually corresponds to 1 bit per second). Nowadays with computers and faster printers it is possible to use faster speeds.

Other improvements have been made in the way data is sent. Computers are widely used now in controlling the sending and receiving of data in quite complicated ways to give more interactive and more reliable communication. Two examples of these methods are packet radio and Amtor.

Amtor

Amtor is widely used on the HF bands. However, it is a comparatively recent development as it was first used in 1978, and developed from a system known as TOR (Telex Over Radio).

The development of Amtor was brought about by the large number of errors which occurred when using RTTY. The conventional way of reducing these errors was to improve the link by increasing the power or improving the aerial system. With the availability of computers another alternative could be used. This was to detect the presence of an error, and ask for any letter or set of letters to be repeated. By doing this the error rate can be dramatically reduced.

In order to understand how Amtor detects errors it is necessary to see how the letters are encoded. When using RTTY each character is converted into a five bit code consisting of digital ones and zeros or marks and spaces. In Amtor a different seven bit code is used. It has been devised so that the number of "ones" always add up to the same number. This means that it is possible for a receiver to check if a character has been received correctly.

In operation the transmitter sends out data three characters at a time. The receiver receives the three characters and analyses them to see if they are correct. At this point the transmitter waits for a reply from the receiver to check that the characters have been received correctly. If they have then the transmitter sends the next block of three characters. If they have not been received correctly then the transmitter repeats them until they are correct.

This mode where an "automatic request for repeat" (ARQ) is used is known as Mode A. However, it can only operate if a receiving station is present. If a station puts out a transmission like a CQ call or news bulletin where he is not actually in contact with another station it will not work. For situations like this a second mode known as Mode B is used. In this case each letter is sent twice with a small time interval in case of noise bursts. By doing this any station will be able to have two attempts at receiving the data, and because seven bits are still transmitted for each character errors can still be detected.

In order to transmit Amtor some equipment apart from the

19

basic transceiver is obviously required. Basically this consists of a display and keyboard together with a terminal unit. Often a home computer can be pressed into service to provide the display and keyboard. The terminal unit is basically a form of modem, and a variety of circuits are available for this. Alternatively it is possible to purchase a ready made one.

When considering the use of Amtor it is worth noting that a fairly fast changeover speed from transmit to receive is required. Whilst most modern equipment is designed to be able to handle Amtor some older units may not be fast enough.

Packet
The other form of data transmission which has become very popular is packet radio. It has become particularly widespread on VHF, but it is also used on HF. Packet has some similarities to Amtor in that it uses error checking techniques, but differs in allowing several stations to use the same frequency by using time sharing techniques, and it also allows the use of repeaters.

As the name implies, a transmission is split up into several packets of data which are sent one at a time. This means that a complete message may need several packets. After each packet is sent the receiver sends an acknowledgement. Then the transmitter waits for the next clear slot on the frequency and then transmits the next packet and so on. If the frequency is clear the waiting time will be comparatively small, but as more stations use the frequency so the waiting time increases.

Each packet of information has a defined format as shown in Figure 2.7. The flags at the beginning and end of each packet are used to provide synchronisation and they have a standard format. Following the first flag the next set of data contains address information, the callsigns of the source station, destination station and any repeaters which may be used are contained here. This means that the message can be ignored by any other stations on the frequency. The next data to be sent is the control byte which is used to signal acknowledgements, requests to repeat the transmission and so forth. Then the message information from the keyboard is transmitted.

Flag	Address	Control	Information	FCS	Flag
8	14/21	1	<256	2	8

Fig. 2.7 The Format of a Packet Transmission

This can be up to 256 bytes long. After this there is the FCS or frame check sequence. Its value is calculated from the data which is sent, and only when the data at the receiver matches the FCS is it accepted and an acknowledgement is transmitted. Finally the terminating flag is sent. This is recognised by the receiver as the termination of the packet.

In the same way that Amtor requires equipment on top of the basic receiver so does packet. The most common approach is to buy or make a terminal node controller (TNC) which controls the functions of the receiver, and organises all the protocols associated with packet. Then a home computer or VDU can be used as a display and keyboard.

Designations
It is very useful to be able to describe the many types of transmission using an easy form of abbreviation. The system which is currently in use was adopted by the World Administrative Radio Conference (WARC) which was held in 1979 and introduced in 1982. The system which was devised superceded a previous one which had been in use for many years and was not able to take account of many of the types of transmission being used. In fact the new system is quite similar in many respects to the old one, but it can more fully describe more types of modulation.

Essentially it consists of three characters as shown in

Figure 2.8. The first describes the type of modulation. e.g., a single sideband, frequency modulation etc. The second describes the signal modulating the carrier, and the third the type of information being transmitted, e.g., telephony, telegraphy etc. As an example it can be seen from the table that single sideband would be denoted as J3E, morse as A1A and FM telephony would be F3E.

In some instances it may also be necessary to state the bandwidth of the signal. This can be done using a four character code consisting of three numbers and a symbol in the place of the decimal point to denote the units — H for Hertz, K for KHz, M for MHz and G for GHz. So a transmission occupying a bandwidth of 3.50 KHz would be represented by 3K50.

First Character *Type of Modulation of Carrier*	Second Character *Nature of Modulating Signal*	Third Character *Type of information to be transmitted*
N An unmodulated carrier	0 No Modulation	N No Information
Amplitude Modulation:	1 Single Channel Quantised or Digital Information	A Telegraphy for Aural Reception
A Double Sideband		B Telegraphy for Automatic Reception
H Single Sideband Full Carrier	2 No Subcarrier	
R Single Sideband Reduced Carrier	2 Single Channel Quantised or Digital Information with Subcarrier	D Data, Telemetry or Telecommand
J Single Sideband Suppressed Carrier	3 Single Channel Analogue Information	C Facsimile
B Independent Sideband		E Telephony
C Vestigial Sideband	7 Two or More Channels Containing Quantised or Digital Information	F Television
Angle Modulation:		W Combination of the above
F Frequency Modulation		X Any Other Cases
G Phase Modulation	9 Composite System Using One or More Channels Containing Quantised Information Together with One or More Using Analogue Information	
D Amplitude and Angle		
Pulse Modulation:		
P Unmodulated Series of Pulses	X Any Other Cases	
K Amplitude Modulated Pulses		
L Pulse Width Modulation		
M Pulse Position Modulation		
Q Angle Modulation During Period of Pulse		
V A Combination of the above		
W A Combination of Two or More, Angle, Amplitude and Pulse Modulation		
X Other Forms of Pulse Modulation		

Fig.2.8 Designation of Radio Transmissions

Chapter 3

CALLSIGNS, CODES AND JARGON

The very nature of radio operating brings with it a lot of codes and jargon. Some of them have arisen as the general jargon which often surrounds any hobby or subject. Other codes have been formulated to enable information, reports and the like to be transmitted quickly and easily over the air. In addition to this many abbreviations have come about because of the widespread use of morse. Obviously when using this mode of transmission it is useful to have a set of abbreviations which can cut down the number of unnecessary letters which have to be sent and increasing the rate at which information can be conveyed. Many of these abbreviations have then been carried over from their use in morse to become part of the everyday vocabulary used by radio amateurs.

Callsigns

One of the first things which will be noticed whilst listening to amateurs on the air is that each station has a callsign. In fact each station is given a unique callsign when it is issued with the licence which it has to possess to operate legally.

The callsign not only serves to identify a particular station, but it can also be used to identify its country. It is even possible sometimes to identify the area in the country where the station is located.

Each callsign consists of two parts: a prefix and a suffix. It is the prefix which gives all the information about where the station is located. The suffix is there to act as a "serial number" for that particular station.

The prefix in a callsign consists of the two or three characters up to and including the last number. For example, in the callsign G3YWX the prefix is G3, or in the callsign VP8ANT the prefix is VP8. By comparing the prefix with a list it is possible to determine the country where the station is located. A shortened list is given in Figure 3.1, and this gives most of the prefixes likely to be encountered on the bands.

Fig.3.1 Amateur Prefix List

A2	Botswana
A4	Oman
A6	United Arab Emirates
A7	Qatar
A9	Bahrain
AA–AG	U.S.A. – see K
AP	Pakistan
BY	China
BV	Taiwan
C3	Andorra
C5	The Gambia
C6	Bahamas
C9	Mozambique
CE	Chile
CN	Morocco
CO	Cuba
CP	Bolivia
CT1	Portugal
CU	Azores
CT3	Madeira
CX	Uraguay
D2	Angola
DA–DL	Germany
DU	Philippines
EA	Spain
EA6	Balearic Islands
EA8	Canary Islands
EA9	Ceuta and Mililla
EI	Eire
EK	Armenia
EL	Liberia
EP	Iran
ET	Ethiopia
ER	Moldova
ES	Estonia
EU	Belarus
EX	Kyrghyzstan
EY	Tadjikistan

Fig.3.1 Amateur Prefix List continued

EZ	Turkmenistan
F	France
FG	Guadeloupe
FM	Martinique
FP	St Pierre and Miquelon
FR	Reunion
FS	French St Martin
G, GX	England
GB	UK Special Event Stations
GD, GT	Isle of Man
GI, GN	Northern Ireland
GJ, GH	Jersey
GM, GS	Scotland
GU, GP	Guernsey
GW, GC	Wales
HA	Hungary
HB	Switzerland
HB0	Leichtenstein
HC	Ecuador
HH	Haiti
HI	Dominican Republic
HK	Colombia
HL	Republic of Korea
HP	Panama
HR	Honduras
HS	Thailand
HV	Vatican City
HZ	Saudi Arabia
I	Italy
J2	Djibouti Republic
JA, JE–JS	Japan
JT	Mongolia
JW	Svalbard
JX	Jan Mayen
JY	Jordan
K, KA–KZ	U.S.A.
AH2, KH2, NH2 WH2	Guam

Fig.3.1 Amateur Prefix List continued

AH6, KH6, NH6 WH6	Hawaii
AL7, KL7, NL7, WL7	Alaska
KP2, NP2, WP2	U.S. Virgin Islands
KP4, NP4, WP4	Puerto Rico
LA	Norway
LU	Argentina
LX	Luxembourg
LZ	Bulgaria
M	United Kingdom – see G
N, NA–NZ	U.S.A. – see K
OA	Peru
OD	Lebanon
OE	Austria
OH	Finland
OH0	Aaland Islands
OJ0	Market Reef
OK	Czech Republic
OM	Slovak Republic
ON	Belgium
OX	Greenland
OY	Faroe Islands
OZ	Denmark
P4	Aruba
PA, PE	Netherlands
PJ1,2,3,4,9	Netherlands Antilles
PJ5,6,7,8	Sint Maarten
PP–PY	Brazil
R, RA–RZ	Russian Federation
S2	Bangladesh
S5	Slovenia
S7	Seychelles
S0	Western Sahara
SK, SL, SM	Sweden
SP	Poland
ST	Sudan
SU	Egypt

Fig.3.1 Amateur Prefix List continued

SV	Greece
T5	Somalia
T7	San Marino
T9	Bosnia Hercegovina
TA	Turkey
TF	Iceland
TG	Guatemala
TI	Costa Rica
TJ	Cameroon
TL	Central African Republic
TN	Congo
TR	Gabon
TT	Chad
TU	Ivory Coast
TY	Benin
TZ	Mali
U, UA–UI	Russian Federation
UK	Uzbekistan
UN	Kazakhstan
UR–UZ	Ukraine
V2	Ukraine
V3	Belize
V4	St Kitts and Nevis
VE, VO, VY, CY	Canada
VP2	Leeward and Windward Islands
VP5	Turks and Caicos Islands
VP8	Falkland Islands, South Georgia, British Antarctic Bases
VP9	Bermuda
VQ9	Chagos
VR6	Pitcairn Islands
VS6, VR2	Hong Kong
VU	India
W, WA–WZ	U.S.A. – see K
XE	Mexico
XU	Kampuchea (Cambodia)
XW	Laos

Fig.3.1 Amateur Prefix List continued

XZ	Myanmar (Burma)
YA	Afghanistan
YB–YD	Indonesia
YI	Iraq
YK	Syria
YL	Latvia
YN	Nicaragua
YO	Romania
YS	El Salvador
YU	Yugoslavia
YV	Venezuela
Z2	Zimbabwe
Z3	Macedonia
ZA	Albania
ZB2	Gibraltar
ZD8	Ascension Island
ZF	Cayman Island
ZL	New Zealand
ZP	Paraguay
ZS	South Africa
2E etc.	Novice licences for the U.K. Letters following the number are the same as for G callsigns, e.g. 2W is Wales
3A	Monaco
3B	Mauritius
3C	Equatorial Guinea
3DA0	Swaziland
3V	Tunisia
3X	Republic of Guinea
4J	Azerbaijan
4L	Georgia
4S	Sri Lanka
4U	United Nations
4W	Republic of Yemen
4X, 4Z	Israel
5A	Libya
5B	Cyprus (ZC4 – British bases on Cyprus)
5H	Tanzania

Fig.3.1 Amateur Prefix List continued

5N	Nigeria
5R	Madagascar
5T	Mauritania
5U	Niger
5V	Togo
5W	Western Samoa
5X	Uganda
5W	Western Samoa
5X	Uganda
5Z	Kenya
6V	Senegal
6Y	Jamaica
7P	Lesotho
7Q	Malawi
7X	Algeria
8P	Barbados
8Q	Maldives
8R	Guyana
9G	Ghana
9H	Malta
9J	Zambia
9K	Kuwait
9L	Sierra Leone
9M	Malaysia
9N	Nepal
9Q	Zaire
9U	Burundi
9V	Singapore
9X	Rwanda
9Y	Trinidad and Tobago

Figure 3.2   U.S.A. Call Areas

Callsign Digit	State
1	Connecticut, Maine, Massachusetts, New Hampshire, Rhode Island, Vermont
2	New Jersey, New York

3	Delaware, District of Columbia, Maryland, Pennsylvania
4	Alabama, Florida, Georgia, Kentucky, North Carolina, South Carolina, Tenessee, Virginia
5	Arkansas, Louisiana, Mississippi, New Mexico, Oklahoma, Texas
6	California
7	Arizona, Idaho, Montana, Nevada, Oregon, Utah, Washington, Wyoming
8	Michigan, Ohio, West Virginia
9	Illinois, Indiana, Wisconsin
0	Colorado, Iowa, Kansas, Minnesota, Missouri, Nebraska, North Dakota, South Dakota

Phonetic Alphabet

When giving callsigns, or spelling out words over the air amateurs or any radio operators will usually use a phonetic alphabet. This is because it is very easy to confuse letters like C and T or M and N which sound quite alike, particularly in the presence of interference. The phonetic alphabet which has been generally adopted is shown in Figure 3.3 However, this is not obligatory and occasionally some people are heard using some other form.

Figure 3.3 The Phonetic Alphabet

A	Alpha	J	Juliett	S	Sierra
B	Bravo	K	Kilo	T	Tango
C	Charlie	L	Lima	U	Uniform
D	Delta	M	Mike	V	Victor
E	Echo	N	November	W	Whisky
F	Foxtrot	O	Oscar	X	X-ray
G	Golf	P	Papa	Y	Yankee
H	Hotel	Q	Queen	Z	Zulu
I	India	R	Romeo		

Q Codes

One of the most generally used codes is the Q code. It is a set of three letter codes all starting with the letter Q and each having its own defined meaning for use as a question or an answer. Some of the codes are intended for maritime uses, whilst others are obviously for aeronautical applications. However, quite a number of them are applicable for amateur use and they are listed in Figure 3.4.

Figure 3.4 The Q Code

QRA	What is the name of your station? The name of my station is
QRB	How far are you from my station? I am about .... from your station
QRG	What is my exact frequency? Your exact frequency is ....
QRH	Does my frequency vary? Your frequency varies
QRI	Does the note of my transmission vary? Your note varies
QRJ	Is my signal weak? Your signals are weak
QRK	What is the readability of my signal? The readability of your signal is ....
QRL	Are you busy? I am busy
QRM	Is there any (man-made) interference? There is (man-made) interference
QRN	Is there any atmospheric noise? There is atmospheric noise
QRO	Shall I increase my power? Increase power

Fig.3.4 The Q Code continued

QRP	Shall I reduce my power? Reduce power
QRQ	Shall I send faster? Send faster
QRS	Shall I send more slowly? Send more slowly
QRT	Shall I stop sending? Stop sending
QRU	Do you have any messages for me? I have nothing for you
QRV	Are you ready to receive? I am ready
QRZ	Who is calling me? You are being called by . . . .
QSK	Can you hear between your signals, i.e., use break in? I can hear between my signals
QSL	Can you acknowledge receipt? I acknowledge receipt
QSP	Can you relay a message? I can relay a message
QSV	Shall I send a series of V's? I will send a series of V's
QSY	Shall I change to another frequency? Change to another frequency
QTH	What is your location? My location is . . . .

Fig.3.4   The Q Code continued

QTR   What is the exact time?
                        The exact time is . . . .

Originally these codes were intended for use with morse transmissions. They were particularly useful because they cut down the number of letters to be sent by a large degree. As they have been used so much, their use has crept into voice communications as well where they are used like any other abbreviation or code.

As the Q code has been used so much it is not always used in its strict question or answer format, particularly in speech. For example it is quite normal to talk about a QRP transmitter meaning a low power transmitter, or to say there is a lot of QRM about, meaning there is a lot of man-made interference. Even so the basic meaning of the code is still maintained.

QSL Cards

One code which has taken on its own particular meaning is QSL. Although it is still used in its traditional sense of confirming reception, it has also come to refer to QSL cards.

They are cards, generally about the size of a postcard, which are sent out by some stations to confirm a contact, as illustrated by Figure 3.5. They have details of the contact, i.e., time, date, frequency etc., and they are often needed when applying for some operating awards. In addition to this some stations have very attractive cards printed which many people mount on the shack wall. Sometimes QSL card collecting can become a secondary interest to the hobby itself.

Some listener stations will also have cards printed. These ones are used to send out reports to stations they have heard in the hope they may receive a QSL card back. When doing this it is advisable to include as many details as possible so that the report is useful, and this will make it more likely that a card will be sent in return.

Abbreviations

There are also a large number of abbreviations which are used in morse or everyday speech. Some have arisen out of the need

G3YWX

OPERATOR: IAN POOLE

TO RADIO _____ CONFIRMING AM/CW SSB QSO OF _____

AT _____ G.M.T. FREQ. _____ MHz YOUR SIGS RST _____

TX: _____ INPUT _____ WATTS

RX: _____ ANTENNA: _____

REMARKS _____

PSE / TKS QSL DIRECT / VIA RSGB _____ 73 de _____

Fig. 3.5 A Typical QSL Card

to abbreviate words or just change the odd letter to make them easier to send in morse. Others have come about as standard abbreviations in general radio use.

Some of them have a certain element of mystery surrounding their origins. A prime example of this is "73" meaning "best regards". One story about this particular one is that the telegraph operators in the last century used to send two dashes, six dots, followed by two dashes as a greeting to one another. As time progressed a space was included in the middle to make two distinct characters, and it adopted the meaning "best regards". Many of the exact origins of some abbreviations are not obvious and have been lost in the mists of time, even so, they are still in everyday use by amateurs all over the world. See Figure 3.6 for a list of abbreviations.

Figure 3.6 Abbreviations

ABT	about
AGN	again
A.M.	amplitude modulation
ANT	antenna
B.C.I.	broadcast interference
BCNU	be seeing you
B.F.O.	beat frequency oscillator
BK	break
B4	before
CFM	confirm
CLD	called
C.I.O.	carrier insertion oscillator
CONDX	condition
CPI	copy
CQ	a general call
CU	see you
CUAGN	see you again
CUD	could
CW	continuous wave (often used to indicate a morse signal)
DE	from
DX	long distance
ERE	here

Fig.3.6 Abbreviations continued

ES	and
FB	fine business
FER	for
F.M.	frequency modulation
FONE	telephony
GA	good afternoon
GB	goodbye
GD	good
GE	good evening
GM	good morning
GN	goodnight
GND	ground
HBREW	home brew
HI	laughter
HPE	hope
HR	here
HV	have
HW	how
LID	poor operator
LW	longwire
MOD	modulation
ND	nothing doing
NW	now
OB	old boy
OM	old man
OP	operator
OT	old timer
P.A.	power amplifier
PSE	please
R	roger (OK)
RCVD	receiver
SA	say
SED	said
SIGS	signals
SRI	sorry
S.S.B.	single sideband
STN	station
S.W.L.	short wave listener

Fig.3.6   Abbreviations continued

TKS	thanks
TNX	thanks
TU	thank you
T.V.I.	television interference
TX	transmitter
U	you
UR	your, you are
VY	very
WID	with
WKD	worked
WUD	would
WX	weather
XMTR	transmitter
XTAL	crystal
XYL	wife
YL	young lady
73	best regards
88	love and kisses

Signal Reports

It is obviously very important to know how one's signals are being received during a contact. It gives a guide to parameters such as band conditions, how well the other station is copying. It also gives an indication of the likelihood of being able to maintain the contact if signals are weak. Another advantage is that it gives a guide to how well the transmitter and even the station as a whole is working. If signal reports are consistently below what is expected it may indicate a fault somewhere.

In order to be able to give concise reports quite easily a signal reporting system has been devised. For a phone or speech transmitter it consists of two numbers to indicate the readability and strength as shown in Figure 3.7. When morse is being used a further number is given to report the tone of the signal. Occasionally this is followed by a further letter to indicate even more about the signal. In this case a C would indicate some chirp on the signal, an X would denote a good crystal controlled signal and K key clicks.

Figure 3.7   RST Code

Readability

1	Unreadable
2	Barely readable
3	Readable with difficulty
4	Readable with little difficulty
5	Totally readable

Strength

1	Faint, barely perceptible
2	Very weak
3	Weak
4	Fair
5	Fairly good
6	Good
7	Moderately strong
8	Strong
9	Very strong

Tone

1	Extremely rough note
2	Very rough note
3	Rough note
4	Rather rough note
5	Strong ripple modulated note
6	Modulated note
7	Near d.c. note but with smooth ripple
8	Good d.c. note with a trace of ripple
9	Pure d.c. note

One example of a report for a moderately strong speech signal which is readable with little difficulty would be 4 7, whereas a strong and perfectly readable morse signal having a pure d.c. note would be 5 8 9.

Morse Code
Morse code must be one of the most famous codes associated with radio. Conceived during the nineteenth century by Samuel Morse the famous inventor and artist, it was widely

used, first on the early telegraph systems and then on radio. In fact, during the early days of radio, it was the only way in which information could be transmitted. However, it did not take long before other modes of transmission started to be used. Even so it continued to be very widely used, and today there is still a large amount of traffic which uses morse. This is particularly true of amateur transmissions on the High Frequency (HF) bands where it forms a very large proportion of the number of transmissions.

The morse code is fairly straightforward, consisting of just dots and dashes as shown in Figure 3.8. However it is essential that the correct spacing is observed otherwise it can become confusing and difficult to read. The dot is taken as the basic length on which everything else is based. The length of a dash is then three times the length of a dot, spacing between dots and dashes is equal to one dot, spacing between letters is three dots, and spacing between words is seven dots, as shown in Figure 3.9.

Amateur contacts in morse make extensive use of abbreviations and codes. This can greatly speed up the rate at which things can be said, but it may make the conversations more difficult to follow at first. As a guide to what might be expected the typical content of a basic contact can be seen in Figure 3.10.

Figure 3.8   International Morse Code

A	. −		N	− .
B	− . . .		O	− − −
C	− . − .		P	. − − .
D	− . .		Q	− − . −
E	.		R	. − .
F	. . − .		S	. . .
G	− − .		T	−
H	. . . .		U	. . −
I	. .		V	. . . −
J	. − − −		W	. − −
K	− . −		X	− . . −
L	. − . .		Y	− . − −
M	− −		Z	− − . .

Fig.3.8   International Morse Code continued

1	. – – –	6	– . . . .
2	. . – – –	7	– – . . .
3	. . . – –	8	– – – . .
4	. . . . –	9	– – – – .
5	. . . . .	0	– – – – –

Full stop	. – . – . –
Comma	– – . . – –
?	. . – – . .
=	– . . . –
Wait	. – . . .
Mistake	. . . .
Stroke (/)	– . . – .

Start of Work ($\overline{\text{CT}}$)	– . – . –
Invitation to Transmit (K)	– . –
End of Work ($\overline{\text{VA}}$)	. . . – . –
End of Message ($\overline{\text{AR}}$)	. – . – .
Invitation for a particular station to transmit ($\overline{\text{KN}}$)	– . – – .

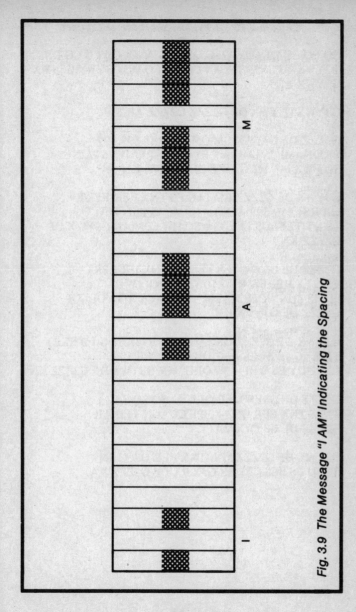

Fig. 3.9 The Message "I AM" Indicating the Spacing

Figure 3.10   A Typical Short Morse Contact

CQ CQ CQ DE G3YWX G3YWX G3YWX CQ CQ CQ DE
G3YWX G3YWX G3YWX CQ CQ CQ DE G3YWX G3YWX
G3YWX AR K

G3YWX G3YWX DE G2ZZZ G2ZZZ AR KN

G2ZZZ DE G3YWX GM OM UR RST 599 599 =
ERE NAME IS IAN IAN ES QTH STAINES STAINES =
SO HW CPI? AT G2ZZZ DE G3YWX KN

G3YWX DE G2ZZZ GM IAN ES TNX FER RPRT =
UR RST 599 599 ALSO = NAME IS TED TED
ES QTH LEEDS LEEDS = SO HW CPI? AR G3YWX DE
G2ZZZ KN

G2ZZZ DE G3YWX FB TED ES TNX UR RPRT =
ERE TX HBREW RNG 10W ES ANT LW =
WX IS SUNNY ES WARM = SO BACK TO YOU AR
G2ZZZ DE G3YWX KN

G3YWX DE G2ZZZ OK IAN UR RIG DOING FB ERE =
TX RNG 100W ES ANT DIPOLE = WX ERE
CLOUDY ES WET = SO QRU? AR G3YWX DE G2ZZZ KN

G2ZZZ DE G3YWX FB QRU ALSO SO SA
73 ES TNX FER QSO = HPE CUAGN TED AR
G2ZZZ DE G3YWX VA

G3YWX DE G2ZZZ MNI TNX FER QSO IAN
BCNU ES BEST 73 AR G3YWX DE G2ZZZ VA

44

Chapter 4

THE H.F. BANDS

The High Frequency (HF) or short wave bands are where most
of the long distance communications take place. Stations
from all over the world can be heard regularly and it is quite
common for contacts to be made with people on the other
side of the world. As a result these bands attract a large
number of stations and this makes them quite crowded at
times. Even so, with today's equipment, and a certain amount
of operating skill the effects of interference can be minimised.

As a result of the number of stations which are active and
the distances over which contacts can be made these bands
can be very interesting. DX chasing or just chatting to people
around the world form part of the HF scene. Another factor
of interest is the study of propagation. This is of particular
importance to the HF operator as it enables him to decide
which band to use, or what areas are likely to be heard at a
given time.

Propagation

The subject of propagation is complicated, but one which can
be very interesting and very rewarding. Even now there are
many aspects about the way in which radio waves are propagated around the earth which are not fully understood. In
fact radio amateurs are still in a position where they are able
to play an important role in helping discover more about
propagation.

Radio waves are very similar to light waves. They can be
reflected and refracted in just the same way. It is because
of this that radio signals from over the horizon and as far
away as the other side of the globe can be heard.

When a signal is transmitted from an aerial it will radiate
out in many directions. Some of the signal will travel along
the ground, and hence it is called a ground wave. This type of
wave is generally used for reception of medium and long wave
transmissions, particularly in the day. This type of propagation can only be used for relatively low frequencies. This is

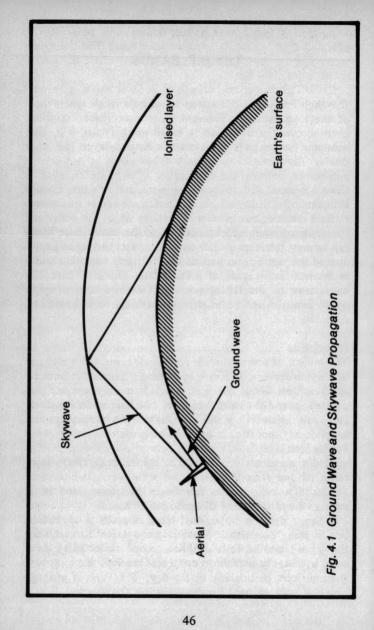

Fig. 4.1 Ground Wave and Skywave Propagation

because it is found that if the transmission frequency is increased much above the medium wave band then the signal becomes attenuated increasingly, to a point where the coverage becomes quite small.

Radio signals can be propagated in other ways. One way in which this happens is when the signals reach the ionised layers above the earth they can be reflected back, returning to the earth at a distant point, as shown in Figure 4.1. This is known as the sky wave and the ionised layers are in a section of the atmosphere called the ionosphere.

The Ionosphere
The ionosphere consists of a number of layers of ionised particles caused by radiation from the sun. The degree of ionisation and hence the properties of the layers is continually changing as a result of a number of factors including the time of day, the season and so forth. It also varies according to the number of sunspots. The reason for this is that it is found that solar radiation is related to the number of spots which are present. As this number tends to follow a cycle of about 11 years propagation conditions are found to follow this pattern.

There are four main layers in the ionosphere, as shown in Figure 4.2. The lowest of them is the D layer which is about 50 Km high. It exists only during the daytime and it is found to absorb low frequency and medium frequency signals. This is why medium wave signals can only be heard over comparatively short distances, whilst at night when it has disappeared signals from much further away can be heard.

The next layer is called the E layer which is about 110 Km high. Signals which are reflected by the E layer generally have a skip distance of up to 2000 Km.

Signals which pass through the E layer then meet the F layer. During the night this consists of a single layer about 200 Km above the earth, but during the day it splits into two, the F_1 layer which remains at about 200 Km altitude, and the F_2 layer at about 300 Km. Signals reflected by these layers have a skip distance of up to 3000 or 4000 Km.

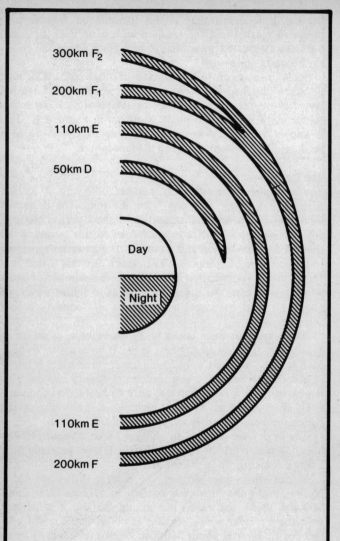

Fig. 4.2 Regions of the Ionosphere

48

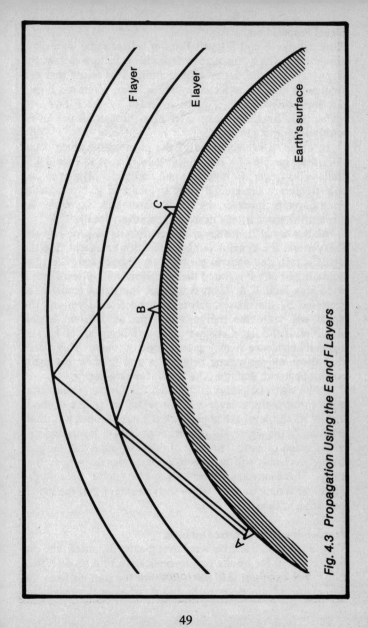

Fig. 4.3 Propagation Using the E and F Layers

49

Signal Propagation

Although the E and F layers bend or refract radio waves, the amount by which this occurs depends on factors such as the frequency and the degree of ionisation. It is found that one frequency may be reflected by the E layer, whereas a higher one may pass through it to be reflected by the F layer. A higher still frequency may even pass through all the layers without returning to earth.

In order to explain some of the phenomena which occur take the example of a transmitter located at A in Figure 4.3. Initially its frequency is set to a point around 1 MHz or so. At this frequency the ground wave is found to give reasonably good coverage, however, the D layer absorbs any sky wave. As a result the signal is only heard comparatively locally.

As the signal frequency increases it starts to penetrate the D layer and the signal is refracted by such an extent that the signal is reflected back to earth by the E layer and is heard at point B. In fact it is found that the signal will be heard over a wide area around B. This is because the signal tends to be scattered by the uneven nature of the ionised layer and the signal will leave the transmitting aerial at different angles. However, if the signal reaches the E or F layers at too high an angle of incidence it may pass straight through. This means that there will be a zone between A and B where the signal cannot be heard, and this is known as the skip zone.

If the signal frequency is increased still further it penetrates right through the E layer and it is reflected by one of the F layers. As this layer is higher the skip distance is much further. Eventually the signal will pass through both F layers and not be reflected to earth. Because of this it is found that the high frequency bands will be able to produce signals from further away. However, they will not always be "open" because the degree of ionisation may fall to such an extent that the signals pass straight through.

Propagation Over Greater Distances

Very often signals will be heard over greater distances than can be accounted for by the simple application of a single reflection. For example, it is quite common for stations from the other side of the globe to be heard, whereas the maximum

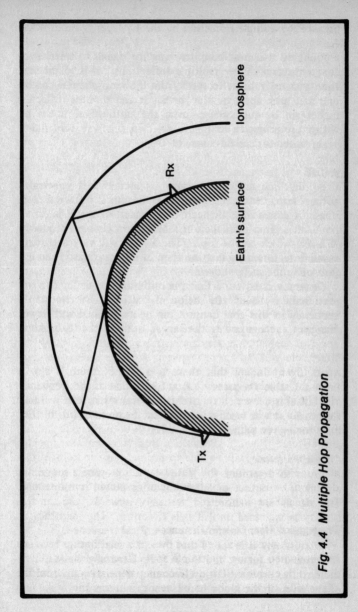

Fig. 4.4 Multiple Hop Propagation

distance for a single reflection by the F_2 layer is about 4000 Km.

Probably the most common way for signals to travel over greater distances is by multiple reflections. It is found that when a signal returns to earth from the ionosphere it can be reflected back again by the earth. It can then be reflected back again by the ionosphere to the earth where it can be picked up as shown in Figure 4.4. In this way very much greater distances can be covered.

M.U.F.

When the frequency of a signal is increased it penetrates further into the ionosphere as it becomes refracted less. Finally it passes right through. As a result of this it is found that over a given path there is a Maximum Usable Frequency (M.U.F.) which can be used. The M.U.F. will vary according to many factors including the time of day, the season and the position in the sunspot cycle.

Generally it is found that the optimum frequency for any given path is about 20% below the M.U.F. By choosing a frequency in this area contact can be maintained with fewer changes to accommodate the varying state of the ionosphere.

L.U.F.

Apart from finding that there is a M.U.F. there is also a Lowest Usable Frequency. It is found that as the frequency of a signal is decreased its strength over a given path will fall. Eventually it will reach a point where it cannot be heard. The limit for a given path is called the L.U.F.

Critical Frequency

In order to determine the state of the ionosphere soundings are taken by various organisations using pulsed transmissions. The signals are transmitted vertically upwards, and the frequency is increased until it fails to return. The frequency at which this happens is known as the critical frequency.

Interestingly it is found that there is a relationship between the critical frequency and the M.U.F. Generally the M.U.F. is three to five times the critical frequency depending upon which of the layers in the ionosphere is being monitored.

H.F. Allocations

Over the HF spectrum there are a number of different frequency bands which are set aside for use by amateurs. Some bands are shared with other services, but in the main this is not so.

The bands are broadly the same over most of the world, although there are some differences between individual countries. The United Kingdom allocations are outlined in Figure 4.5a whilst the frequencies available in the U.S.A. are given in Figure 4.5b.

The amateur bands in the HF spectrum cover a wide range of frequencies from 1.8 MHz at the low end to just under 30 MHz at the top. This means that it is possible to make use of different types of propagation and also to make the best use of the prevailing conditions. Another feature of the wide spread of frequencies is that each band will have its own characteristics. By knowing a little about each band it is possible to have a good idea about what is likely to be heard and how to make the best use of each band.

1.81 – 2.0 MHz (160 metres)

This band is also referred to as "Top Band" as it is the band with the largest wavelength (and lowest frequency). It is shared with other services, mainly ship to shore communications, but this does not normally cause too much interference. Because it is shared many countries do not have an allocation here, or it may be very much smaller.

Generally contacts over distances of up to 50 miles can be made without difficulty during the day, and this extends up to distances of up to a few hundred miles at night. With good aerials it is possible to make contacts over two or three thousand miles and very occasionally to the other side of the world. However, its main use is as a local "natter" band and it is quite common to hear club nets or the like.

3.50 – 3.80 MHz (80 metres)

Again this band is shared with other services, but most countries do have an allocation here. In fact, in the U.S.A. it extends up to 4.0 MHz. Owing to the fact it is shared it can become very congested particularly at night. Even so it is

Figure 4.5   H.F. Frequency Allocations

(a) UNITED KINGDOM

1.810 –	2.000 MHz
3.500 –	3.800 MHz
7.000 –	7.100 MHz
10.100 –	10.150 MHz
14.000 –	14.350 MHz
18.068 –	18.168 MHz
21.000 –	21.450 MHz
24.890 –	24.990 MHz
28.000 –	29.700 MHz

(b) U.S.A.

1.800 –	2.000 MHz
3.500 –	4.000 MHz
7.000 –	7.300 MHz
10.100 –	10.150 MHz
14.000 –	14.350 MHz
21.000 –	21.450 MHz
24.890 –	24.990 MHz
28.000 –	29.700 MHz

possible to use it without too much interference.

During the day it is quite possible to reach distances of a couple of hundred miles, and after dark distances of a thousand miles or so are quite common. It is also possible to make contacts over much greater distances and even to the opposite side of the world. One particularly good time for DX is at dawn or dusk.

Although this band is being used increasingly for DX working it still primarily remains a "natter" band, particularly during the day.

7.00 – 7.10 MHz (40 metres)

On forty metres it is possible to hear stations at greater distances than on eighty during the day. Stations at five hundred miles distance or more are common and during the night intercontinental contacts are quite easy. Again more distant contacts are possible, particularly at night.

The band used to be plagued by high power broadcast stations. Fortunately this is no longer the case on frequencies up to 7.1 MHz. However, broadcast stations in some parts of the world are still allowed to use the section between 7.1 to 7.3 MHz which is allocated to amateurs in some countries.

10.10 – 10.15 (30 metres)
This band was released for amateur use as a result of the World Administrative Radio Conference (WARC) held in 1979. It only has a small bandwidth and is not yet well established. As a result it is not as well used as many of the other bands. Even so it can produce contacts over a thousand miles or so most days, and intercontinental contacts at certain times of the day.

14.00 – 14.35 (20 metres)
This is one of the most popular DX bands and as such it often becomes quite congested. However, it is open most days to many distant parts of the globe and will usually produce contacts with stations in Europe. During the winter, especially at low points in the sunspot cycle, the band will close after dark, but during the summer it will often remain open all night. Like many other bands best conditions for contacts to the other side of the globe will be at dawn and dusk, although good DX contacts can often be made at any time.

18.068 – 18.168 (17 metres)
Like 30 metres this band was released after WARC in 1979 and because of this it is not as popular as many of the more established bands. Despite this it is a very useful band and can offer the possibility of good DX although it can only be used for CW. It is not unlike 20 metres offering DX from all over the world for a large portion of the day. However, it is more prone to seasonal and daily changes.

21.00 – 21.45 MHz (15 metres)
This is another very popular DX band. Whilst it is not open as consistently as 20 metres it still carries DX traffic for a large

portion of the day. In view of the higher frequency the skip distance is longer and this means that intereference from shorter range stations (under 1000 Km) is less than on 20 metres.

24.89 – 24.99 (12 metres)
Again this band is another new one released after WARC '79. In character it is a half-way house between ten and fifteen metres. It is very dependent on seasonal and other propagation changes. However, it produces some good DX when it is open.

28.00 – 29.70 MHz (10 metres)
This band can be particularly interesting. Not only does it support the usual modes of HF propagation, but it is also subject to other modes more usually associated with VHF. It is very dependent upon seasonal and sunpot changes, sometimes appearing dead, whilst at other times spring into life to produce some very good DX. Often very good DX contacts can be made using surprisingly low power levels and small aerials.

There are also a wide variety of transmission modes which are used on Ten. CW and SSB are widely used as DX modes. Then in the upper section of the band there is a growing interest in the use of FM. One of the reasons for this is that it is quite easy to convert 27 MHz CB rigs to use these frequencies. This makes it an easy and cheap way of getting on the air.

Band Plans
Within the amateur bands there are certain sections and spot frequencies which are reserved for different types of transmission. For example, the bottom section of the band is reserved for CW or morse operation. In addition to this other areas or spot frequencies are reserved for beacons. The reason for planning the bands in this way is to make the best use of the available space so that the wider bandwidth modes like SSB do not occupy all the available space.

In most countries these band plans are purely advisory. Even so it is found that most people adhere to them quite strictly. For this reason it is very rare to hear an SSB station in the CW end of the band, however, it is perfectly permissible to resort to CW in the phone section. This is because CW is a narrow band mode and can be used in amongst sideband signals without causing any extra interference, whereas the reverse is most certainly not true.

Band plans are essentially quite straightforward. The region 1 band plan is shown in Figure 4.6. It shows the various types of transmission which are advised and the frequencies reserved for them.

In the U.S.A. the situation is rather different as the licence states what modes can be used in particular sections of the band. In addition to this a form of incentive licensing is employed with the more advanced licencees being allowed access to more frequencies, or allowed to use modes like SSB in more sections of the band. However, as a guide to which sections of the band are likely to contain the various types of signal from the States an overall band plan is given in Figure 4.7.

QRP
One aspect of amateur radio which has become very popular over the last few years amongst HF CW enthusiasts is QRP or low power operation. The challenge of making contacts on low power seems to have caught the imagination of many people. In addition to this many circuits for QRP CW equipment are quite simple and straightforward. This means that it is quite within the capabilities of most people to build their own equipment. In fact a wide variety of designs for two or three transistor transmitters have appeared in the magazines over the years. Using these transmitter designs many people have been able to build it in one evening and been on the air the next.

In order to give stations running low power transmitters a better chance against the interference and to enable them to talk to other low power stations certain QRP calling frequencies have been set aside. Generally they are 60 KHz from the bottom end of the band as listed in Figure 4.8. However it will be seen that this is not so on 40 metres and 30 metres where the size of the band does not allow this.

Figure 4.6   Region 1 HF Band Plan

3.500 –	3.600	CW
3.590 –	3.610	RTTY
3.600 –	3.800	CW and Phone
3.730 –	3.740	SSTV
7.000 –	7.040	CW
7.035 –	7.045	RTTY and SSTV
7.040 –	7.100	CW and Phone
10.100 –	10.150	CW
10.140 –	10.150	RTTY
14.000 –	14.100	CW
14.080 –	14.100	RTTY
14.100		Beacon
14.100 –	14.350	CW and Phone
14.225 –	14.235	SSTV
18.068 –	18.110	CW
18.100 –	18.110	RTTY
18.110 –	18.168	CW and Phone
21.000 –	21.150	CW
21.080 –	21.020	RTTY
21.150 –	21.450	CW and Phone
21.335 –	21.345	SSTV
24.890 –	24.930	CW
24.920 –	24.930	RTTY
24.930 –	24.990	CW and Phone
28.000 –	28.200	CW
28.050 –	28.150	RTTY
28.200 –	29.700	CW and Phone
28.550 –	26.265	SSTV

Figure 4.7   U.S.A. HF Band Plan

3.500 –	3.750	CW
3.750 –	4.000	CW and Phone
7.000 –	7.150	CW
7.150 –	7.300	CW and Phone
10.100 – 10.150		CW
14.000 – 14.150		CW
14.150 – 14.350		CW and Phone
21.000 – 21.200		CW
21.200 – 21.450		CW and Phone
24.890 – 24.930		CW
24.930 – 24.990		CW and Phone
28.000 – 28.300		CW
28.300 – 29.700		CW and Phone

Figure 4.8   QRP Calling Frequencies

Band	Frequency (MHz)
80	3.560
40	7.030
30	10.106
20	14.060
15	21.060
10	28.060

Whilst there are no hard and fast definitions about the power limits for QRP operation various organisations do have their own limits for any contests or awards they organise. In general the limit is 10 watts DC input or 5 watt RF output.

Even so there is no reason why lower powers cannot be used. In fact many people have made contacts over considerable distances using powers of less than a watt.

Chapter 5

VHF AND UHF BANDS

Technically the VHF part of the frequency spectrum stretches
from 30 MHz up to 300 MHz, and the UHF part falls between
300 MHz and 3000 MHz. In the VHF and UHF bands there
are a number of amateur allocations. Generally their characteristics are quite different to those of the HF bands for a
number of reasons. Firstly signal propagation uses different
modes. Also basic aerial lengths are shorter making it possible
to make much more directive aerials. On top of this constructional techniques are different. As a result these bands have
their own group of ardent followers who gain every bit as
much enjoyment from VHF and UHF as those who find the
lower frequencies their field of interest.

Propagation
When listening on any of the VHF or UHF bands, it will be
quickly noticed that the propagation is totally different to the
HF bands. Stations are generally heard up to a hundred miles
or a little more, unless there is a lift in conditions. When these
lifts occur stations can be heard at much greater distances. It
is knowing how to predict them that adds interest to these
frequencies and enables many stations to contact more DX.
  There are several mechanisms by which signals can be
propagated over greater than normal distances. Tropo (or
tropospheric ducting), sporadic E, aurora and meteor scatter
are the most used. Each mechanism has its own trade marks,
and each has some give away signs or times when it is most
likely to occur. In order to have a better idea about predicting
each type it is necessary to look at the way signals are propagated, first under normal or "flat" band conditions and then
when they are propagated by each mode in turn.

Line of Sight
This is the mode of communication which is present most of
the time. When it is the only form of propagation present
conditions are said to be flat. Despite this communications can

be made over distances much greater than the actual line of sight distance itself.

The reason for this extra distance is that the refractive index of the air changes with the altitude. In the lower atmosphere the air is more dense than it is at higher altitudes. This has an effect on its refractive index which in turn has an effect on the radio waves. In the same way as light bends towards an area of higher refractive index it is found that the radio signals will bend slightly to follow the earth curvature. In this way they will be heard over distances which greatly exceed the true line of sight.

Tropospheric Ducting

Often band conditions can be changed dramatically by weather conditions in the troposphere, i.e., the area of atmosphere up to about 10 Km from the earth's surface. Generally it is found that the air temperature decreases with rising altitude. However, when there are areas of high pressure or cold fronts over the country and on cold frosty mornings it is possible that temperature inversions occur. When this happens the air nearer the earth's surface is colder than the air above it. This makes the air nearer the earth's surface even more dense than usual and the air higher up less dense. In turn this results in the change in refractive index being much larger than normal and makes the refraction of radio waves much more pronounced. Under these conditions signals can be heard over much greater distances than is normally possible.

Sporadic E (E_s)

Sporadic E is one of the more spectacular forms of propagation to affect the VHF bands. When it occurs stations up to about 2000 Km can be heard with little difficulty. However, as can be seen from the name this mode of propagation is not easy to predict and does not last for long.

It occurs when a cloud of very intense ionisation forms in the E layer. Generally a cloud is about 100 Km across, but only a few tens of metres thick. As it forms its intensity builds up and it reflects signals with progressively higher frequencies. As a result the 50 MHz and 70 MHz bands are affected first and then it is possible that 2 metres may be affected. On very rare occasions it has been known for the 220 MHz band in the U.S.A. to support sporadic E propagation.

The length of time the opening lasts is very dependent on the frequency in use and the intensity of the ionisation. At lower frequencies it will remain open for much longer and as the frequency increases it becomes shorter. On two metres it is rare for the band to support sporadic E propagation for more than two hours and it is not uncommon for an opening to last as little as ten minutes or so.

To add to the sporadic nature of this mode of propagation the ionised clouds move as they are blown around in the air currents in the upper atmosphere. This means that the areas to which the opening exists will change. Also beam headings will have to be changed during the opening.

Very little is known about the mechanism which causes sporadic E and it is not possible to predict when they will occur. All that can be said is that it occurs in the summer with the months of June and July providing the best openings.

Aurora

The Northern Lights or Aurora Borealis are not only a spectacular sight, but they also give a good indication of the possibility of propagation by Aurora.

Both the lights themselves and the mode of propagation are caused by the same effect — areas of intense ionisation around the poles. They form during periods of high solar activity when streams of highly charged particles are emitted by the sun. If these streams enter the earth's atmosphere then the Northern Lights can be seen. Another result is that there is a large increase in the level of ionisation in the region of the F layer around the poles. This ionisation can be so intense that it is possible for signals with frequencies up to around 150 MHz to be reflected.

During an "Auroral Event" the ionisation is very uneven, and it also changes. As a result of this, signals reflected by the ionised layer can reach the receiver via several different paths. It is also found that the changing nature of the ionisation adds a varying doppler shift to the signal. These two effects combine to give a very distinctive sound to any signal which is reflected. This often means that it is easier to use CW, although if signals are very strong it is possible to use SSB.

The distances which can be covered using auroral propagation vary widely because of the way in which the reflection takes place. However, as a rough guide the maximum likely to be achieved is around 2000 Km.

Prediction of exact times when an aurora will occur is not possible. However, the best times to be on the look out are in March and September in the evening at around sunset.

Meteor Scatter
This form of propagation is not used by many operators because it requires the use of higher powers, very directive aerials, sensitive receivers and special operating procedures. In spite of this it can produce good results when band conditions would normally be flat, and it is an interesting form of propagation to use.

Meteor scatter is possible because the earth's atmosphere is continually being bombarded by meteors. Even though there are only a few large ones which leave visible trails there are many more smaller ones which are not visible. However, all of these meteors will leave a trail of ionisation which can reflect radio waves and it is at about the same height as the E layer. Sometimes the ionisation can last for up to two minutes if the meteor is large, but if it is small it may only last for a second or so.

The ionisation is very intense and can reflect radio signals into the VHF section of the spectrum. However, the top frequency limit means that 2 metres is the highest frequency band where meteor scatter can be used.

Using meteor scatter contacts may be made over distances of up to 2000 Km or so, but as the signal levels are so low and ionisation trails are so short, contacts are usually pre-arranged.

Although meteor scatter is not subject to the same variations as other modes of propagation there are still some seasonal changes. This happens because the earth passes through various clouds or concentrations of meteors around the sun. This means that the time when a particular cloud or shower will arrive can be judged quite accurately.

The VHF and UHF Bands

There are several amateur bands in the VHF/UHF section of the frequency spectrum. Their characteristics vary quite widely dependent upon where they are in the spectrum. On top of this the size of the bands may be different, one occupying as little as 250 KHz whilst others are several megahertz wide. Also the allocation of the bands differs from one country to the next. This results in some bands being larger or only available in certain countries and not in others.

6 Metres   50 – 52 MHz   (50 – 54 MHz in U.S.A.)
This band can be particularly interesting because it exhibits the qualities of HF and VHF bands. Under flat band conditions distances of around 100 miles can be achieved fairly easily. Then during the summer months it is found that sporadic E affects it quite frequently. On top of this during the peaks in the sunspot cycle signals can be reflected by the F_2 layer making it possible to achieve world wide communication.

The band is not allocated in all countries. It is very popular in the U.S.A. and Canada and now it is being made available in several European countries, including the U.K., with the decline of VHF television.

4 Metres   70.25 – 70.50 MHz
This band is available in comparatively few countries, the U.K. being one. In view of this there is not the usual variety of commercially made equipment. As a result a high proportion of people who use home brewed equipment, or units converted from private mobile radio use it. This all adds to the interest of the band which can produce some interesting contacts over long distances at times.

2 Metres   144 – 146 MHz   (144 – 148 MHz in U.S.A.)
This is probably the most popular band in this part of the frequency spectrum. Aerials are reasonably sized and equipment is readily available making it easily accessible. The widespread network of repeaters, and the fact that up until recently it was the lowest frequency band available to Class B licencees in the U.K., have all added to its popularity.

The propagation and possibility of DX add to the interest of the band. Whilst under flat band conditions stations can be contacted up to fifty miles or more, the presence of tropo and sporadic E means that it is possible to make contacts over much greater distances.

140 cms   220 – 225 MHz (U.S.A. only)
This band is not available in Europe but is very popular in the U.S.A. Its character is very much that of a "half-way house" between two metres and 70 centimetres. Tropo is the main propagation mode for DX. Sporadic E which gives some of the most spectacular results on 2 does not normally affect the band although it has been known on rare occasions.

70 cms   432 – 440 MHz (430 – 450 MHz U.S.A.)
Seventy "cems" is another popular band for local communication. There is a large network of repeaters in most countries making it very popular amongst FM and mobile enthusiasts, particularly when two metres is crowded.

The propagation is similar to that found on 2 metres although sporadic E is not encountered. To balance this, it is found that tropo can be better, and can often mean DX contacts can be made on 70 when they are more difficult to make on two.

Band Plans
The VHF and UHF bands serve to fulfil a large number of requirements. Not only are they used for local or crosstown contacts, but there is a large amount of mobile operation. Then they are used by DX chasers as well as the more specialised interests like satellite communications and so forth. There are also a wide variety of modes which are used, from SSB to FM and speech to packet radio. As a result it has been found that it is necessary to split the bands into segments so that different forms of communication do not interfere with one another and operation is made easier.

Figures 5.1 to 5.4 show the different band plans which have been devised. From them it can be seen that the bands have been split into different sections dependent upon the type of mode in use. In addition to this, sections of the bands are set aside for beacons and specialised uses like satellite communication. By splitting the bands in this manner the best use is made of the available spectrum.

Figure 5.1   Region 1: 6 Metre Band Plan

50.000 − 50.080	CW and Beacons
50.080 − 50.100	CW only
50.100 − 51.000	Narrow band modes (CW, SSB, AM, RTTY, SSTV etc.)
50.200	SSB calling frequency
50.600	RTTY calling frequency
51.000 − 51.100	Pacific DX window (narrow band only)
51.100 − 52.000	All modes (including FM and repeaters)
52.000 − 52.100	Pacific DX window (narrow band only)
52.100 − 54.000	All modes (including FM and repeaters)

Figure 5.2   U.K.: 70 MHz Band Plan

70.025 − 70.075	Beacons
70.075 − 70.150	CW
70.150 − 70.260	SSB
70.200	SSB calling frequency
70.260 − 70.400	All modes
70.260	Mobile calling frequency
70.300	RTTY calling frequency
70.400 − 70.500	FM
70.450	FM calling frequency

Figure 5.3   Region 1: 2 Metre Band Plan

144.000 – 144.150	CW only
144.000 – 144.025	Moon bounce
144.050	CW calling frequency
144.100	Meteor Scatter (CW)
144.150 – 144.500	SSB and CW
144.300	SSB calling frequency
144.400	Meteor Scatter (SSB)
144.500 – 144.845	All modes
144.500	Slow Scan TV calling frequency
144.600	RTTY
144.675	Data Modes calling frequency
144.700	Fax calling frequency
144.750	ATV calling and talkback
144.845 – 144.900	Beacons
145.000 – 145.800	FM Simplex and Repeaters
145.500 (S20)	FM calling frequency
145.800 – 146.000	Satellite Operation

Figure 5.4   Region 1: 70 Cms Band Plan

431.025 – 431.450	Repeater Input for 7.6 MHz shift
432.000 – 432.150	CW only
432.000 – 432.025	Moon bounce
432.050	Centre of CW activity
432.150 – 432.500	SSB and CW
432.200	Centre of SSB activity
432.350	Microwave talkback
432.500 – 432.800	All modes
432.500	Centre of Slow Scan TV activity
432.600	Centre of RTTY activity
432.675	Centre of Data Modes activity
432.700	Centre of Fax activity
432.800 – 432.990	Beacons
433.000 – 433.225	Repeater Channels for 1.6 MHz Shift
433.300	RTTY
433.400 – 433.575	Simplex
433.500 (SU20)	FM calling frequency
433.600 – 435.000	Repeater Channels for 1.6 MHz Shift
435.000 – 438.000	Satellite Operation
438.000 – 439.050	Repeater Output for 7.6 MHz Shift
439.050 – 440.000	TV operation

Channels

Operation on these bands is often channelised. For SSB and CW calling frequencies or channels that are set aside for CQ calls or calls to specific stations. Once contact has been established the stations move off to a mutually agreed frequency. By using calling channels it means that the necessity for tuning up and down the band to find stations calling CQ is eliminated.

For FM all the operating is channelised, as shown by Figures 5.5 and 5.6. The FM section of the band is split up into channels spaced 25 KHz apart. This spacing was chosen because it is sufficient to prevent stations on one channel interfering with the next.

Each channel is designated a number. Simplex ones start with the letter S for 2 metres or SU for 70 cms, e.g., S20 is a 2 metre channel number and is in fact the calling channel, or

SU20 is the calling channel on 70 cms. Repeater channels are numbered in the same way but commence with R for 2 metres or RU on 70 cms. In the U.K. on 70 cms, repeater channels are designated by the letters RB. This is because the input channels occupy the higher frequencies instead of the lower ones.

Figure 5.5   Two Metre Channel Designations

Frequency	Channel	
145.000	R0	
145.025	R1	
145.050	R2	
145.075	R3	REPEATER INPUTS
145.100	R4	
145.125	R5	
145.150	R6	
145.175	R7	
145.200	S8	
145.225	S9	
145.250	S10	
145.275	S11	
145.300	S12	
145.325	S13	
145.350	S14	
145.375	S15	SIMPLEX CHANNELS
145.400	S16	
145.425	S17	
145.450	S18	
145.475	S19	
145.500	S20	
145.525	S21	
145.550	S22	
145.575	S23	
145.600	R0	
145.625	R1	
145.650	R2	
145.675	R3	REPEATER OUTPUTS
145.700	R4	
145.725	R5	
145.750	R6	
145.775	R7	

Figure 5.6   Seventy Centimetre Channel Designations

433.000	RB0	
433.025	RB1	
433.050	RB2	
433.075	RB3	
433.100	RB4	
433.125	RB5	
433.150	RB6	
433.175	RB7	REPEATER CHANNELS
433.200	RB8	
433.225	RB9	
433.250	RB10	
433.275	RB11	
433.300	RB12	
433.325	RB13	
433.350	RB14	
433.375	RB15	
433.400	SU16	
433.424	SU17	
433.450	SU18	
433.475	SU19	
433.500	SU20	SIMPLEX CHANNELS
433.525	SU21	
433.550	SU22	
433.575	SU23	
433.600	SU24	
434.600	RB0	
434.625	RB1	
434.650	RB2	
434.675	RB3	
434.700	RB4	
434.725	RB5	REPEATER CHANNELS
434.750	RB6	
434.775	RB7	
434.800	RB8	
434.825	RB9	
434.850	RB10	

Fig.5.6   Seventy Centimtre Channel Designations continued

434.875	RB11	
434.900	RB12	
434.925	RB13	REPEATER CHANNELS
434.950	RB14	
434.975	RB15	

Repeater Channels

Mobile operation has become very popular on the VHF and UHF bands. In fact by far the greatest proportion of mobile stations use either 2 metres or 70 cms. There are several reasons for this but one of the major advantages if the relative ease with which efficient aerials can be made at these frequencies.

The popularity of these bands for mobile use has lead to a network of repeaters being set up. The idea of a repeater is to enable mobile or portable units to be able to communicate over greater distances. This is possible because the repeater is located on a local high point. This makes it possible for the repeater to receive the weak mobile stations, and then re-transmit the signal so that it can be heard over a wider range.

The repeater operates by receiving signals on the input channel. It then changes the frequency of the signal and re-transmits it on the output channel. As a result of this "repeater shift" stations have to transmit on one frequency and listen on another. Generally the shift is 600 KHz on 2 metres and 1.6 MHz on 70 cms.

In order to access a repeater it is usual for them to require an audio tone. Generally a tone burst of 1750 Hz lasting for about half a second is required. The reason for this is to prevent noise or other spurious signals from being re-radiated. Most repeaters only require the use of a tone burst to open it when it is in its quiescent state. The tone is then not needed again until the contact has finished and the repeater has returned to its quiescent state.

Chapter 6

RECEIVERS

There are a large number of different types of receiver on the market these days. The ways in which they operate can vary and so can the specifications which they meet.

Most people interested in amateur radio want some form of communications receiver. From the name it can be gathered that they are generally used for receiving long distance or communications type transmissions. These might include shortwave broadcast stations, amateur transmissions, citizen's band and so forth. The design of these receivers is far superior to that of an ordinary broadcast receiver; they have a high degree of stability (i.e., the frequency does not drift); they are very selective (i.e., they are able to reject unwanted stations slightly off frequency); they are able to resolve several different types of transmission, e.g., AM, SSB CW and sometimes FM; they also cover a wide range of frequencies (a typical communications receiver covers 0.5 to 30 MHz).

Another type of receiver which is becoming very popular is the scanner. It is generally used for frequencies above 30 MHz and although it broadly uses the same principles as a communications receiver, its style of operation is different. As most of the operation above 30 MHz is channelised, i.e., transmissions every 25 KHz it is possible to design the receiver so it will tune directly to these frequencies. This makes it very easy to quickly tune, or scan a number of channels to see what can be heard.

Receivers can also employ a number of different principles. For example there are TRF (tuned radio frequency) receivers, direct conversion ones, as well as superhets. All of them are used at the moment, or they have been in the past. They all have their own advantages and disadvantages.

The TRF Receiver

The TRF or tuned radio frequency receiver is little used today because of its shortcomings. However, in the early days of radio they were used almost exclusively. Today their lack of sensitivity and selectivity means that more advanced designs

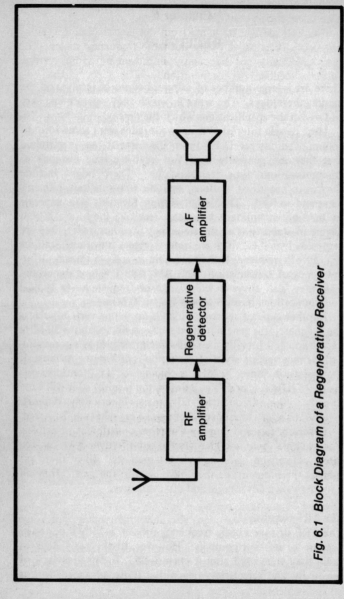

Fig. 6.1 Block Diagram of a Regenerative Receiver

74

have taken their place.

The TRF derives its name from the fact that all the tuning or selectivity is provided by the radio frequency stages. The basic selectivity can be greatly improved by adding various forms of feedback, or regeneration.

The basic regenerative receiver uses an oscillating detector as shown in Figure 6.1. This provides a very large increase in sensitivity as well as selectivity. A regeneration control is included so that the detector can be adjusted to be just on the point of oscillating for reception of AM signals. If CW or SSB signals are to be resolved the detector is made to oscillate so that a beat note is obtained.

The regenerative receiver circuits often contain an RF amplifier to give some amplification of the signal at radio frequencies. This is followed by the regenerative detector which converts the signal from radio frequencies to audio. It also gives most of the amplification. Finally the audio signal is amplified to drive either a loudspeaker or headphones.

The next development of the TRF is called the super-regenerative receiver. This type of receiver again has a regenerative detector but the regeneration is interrupted by a signal just above the audible range. Using this idea receivers with remarkably good sensitivity and selectivity can be made. In fact their performance was so good that they were very popular for use at VHF and UHF up until the early 1960's. Unfortunately they cannot be made as selective as other types of receiver and as a result they fell into disuse.

Apart from the lack of selectivity another major disadvantage of the regenerative type of receiver is that they can cause interference to other listeners. The oscillating detector can radiate quite considerable distances, particularly if no stage of RF amplification is present to isolate the aerial from the detector.

Direct Conversion Receivers

This type of receiver was also developed many years ago during the First World War. Despite the age of the basic concept it still has its place amongst today's receivers, and it is particularly popular with QRP operators. This is because direct conversion receivers can offer a performance which is

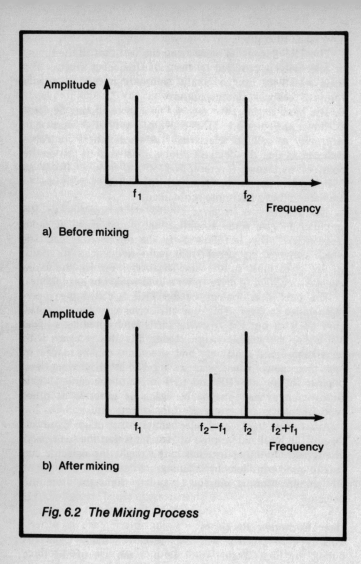

Amplitude

f_1 f_2
Frequency

a) Before mixing

Amplitude

f_1 f_2-f_1 f_2 f_2+f_1
Frequency

b) After mixing

Fig. 6.2 The Mixing Process

76

able to cope with today's crowded band conditions whilst still remaining relatively simple and easy to construct.

The direct conversion receiver, or DCRX for short, uses a mixer like many other pieces of radio equipment. Essentially this is a non-linear device into which two radio frequency signals are injected. It is found that when this is done extra signals are generated at frequencies corresponding to the sum and difference of the two original ones, as shown in Figure 6.2. So it can be seen that mixing a signal of 10 MHz with another one of 1 MHz results in extra signals at 11 MHz and 9 MHz being produced. This phenomenen is very useful and is used in very many ways.

In the DCRX it is used to convert the frequency of the incoming signal from its radio frequency right down to an audio frequency. In this way, tuning the frequency of the second signal or local oscillation as it is called to one slightly different to that of the incoming signal, an audio beat is obtained. This is obviously ideal for resolving morse signals. It is also possible to resolve SSB signals in this manner. AM signals can be resolved by tuning the local oscillator to the same frequency as the incoming carrier and obtaining a "zero beat". Unfortunately it is not possible to resolve FM.

A typical block diagram of a direct conversion receiver is given in Figure 6.3. After leaving the aerial the signal is immediately presented to the preselector or RF tuning. This is needed to ensure that only signals of approximately the right frequency are presented to the mixer. This reduces the likelihood of very strong off-channel signals like broadcast stations or local radio amateurs from overloading the mixer. This could result in them breaking straight through into the audio stages regardless of the tunings.

It is possible that this stage may have some amplification. Not only will this provide an increase in signal strength, but it will also reduce any of the local oscillator signal which may reach the aerial and radiate causing interference to others.

Once through the preselector it reaches the mixer. Here it is mixed with the signal from the local oscillator to produce the audio signal. Often this stage will use a type of mixer which produces some gain.

The local oscillator which is injected into the mixer has to

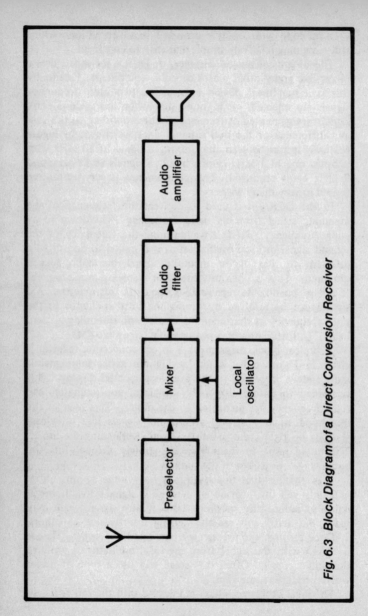

Fig. 6.3 Block Diagram of a Direct Conversion Receiver

78

be very stable because the frequency stability of the receiver is totally dependent upon it. If it drifts by as little as 100 Hz then the audio tone of whatever is being received will also change by 100 Hz.

The signal from the mixer is generally passed into a low pass filter. This is to remove any unwanted high frequency audio signals. Its cutoff frequency is generally made to be about 3 KHz as this is perfectly acceptable for speech. Often if the receiver is to be used for morse reception a sharp band-pass filter centred around 750 Hz is used. This gives the added selectivity to be able to pick stations out when the band is very crowded.

Once the signal leaves the audio filters it can be amplified to feed either a loudspeaker or headphones.

The main disadvantages of the direct conversion receiver is what is called the audio image. It is found that a beat note is obtained when tuning to either side of a signal, i.e., a tone of say 700 Hz below the wanted signal or 700 Hz above it. In spite of this disadvantage many people find that they like this type of receiver because of its simplicity and cost effectiveness.

The Superheterodyne Receiver

The type of receiver which is most commonly used nowadays is called the superheterodyne or superhet receiver. It is more complicated than the other types which have already been described but its advantages far outweigh the extra cost of its complexity. As a result the superhet is used in virtually all the transistor portables, communications receivers, televisions, scanners and other radios on the market today.

One of the major problems encountered in receiver designs is that of providing sufficient selectivity whilst retaining enough flexibility of operation. This problem is only partly solved in the TRF receiver by using a regenerative detector. The DC receiver attempts to solve it by directly converting the signals down to audio frequencies and using simple audio filters. Unfortunately the way in which it operates is not always suitable, especially if AM or FM signals are to be resolved.

The superhet overcomes all of these problems. It can be made as selective as required, and it can also be made to resolve

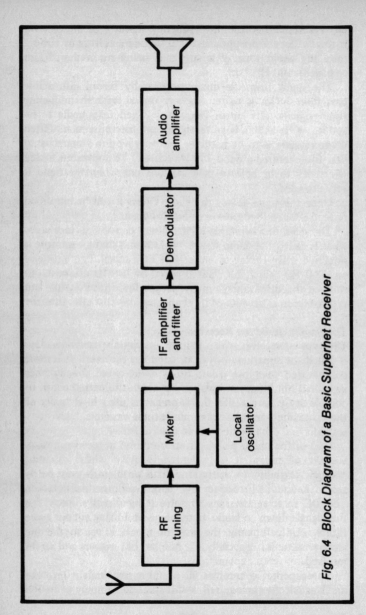

Fig. 6.4 Block Diagram of a Basic Superhet Receiver

any type of transmission by using the correct type of detector. In fact it is possible to make multimode receivers by simply installing the relevant detectors and switching in the correct one for the mode in use.

Essentially the superhet operates by having a variable frequency local oscillator. This is mixed with the incoming signals to convert them down to a fixed intermediate frequency (IF) stage. Here the signals are filtered and amplified using a fixed frequency filter. By varying the frequency of the local oscillator the signals which will be converted to the exact frequency of the IF stages will change. For example, if a receiver has an intermediate frequency of 455 KHz and the local oscillator frequency is set to 1000 KHz then signals on 1455 KHz will be received. By moving the local oscillator up to 1100 KHz, signals of a frequency of 1555 KHz will be picked up. A block diagram of a basic superhet receiver is shown in Figure 6.4.

There are a number of advantages to having a fixed intermediate frequency section. Firstly the filter design and construction is greatly simplified. In addition to this the filter performance is much better. This is because it is very much simpler to make a fixed frequency filter having the several sections needed to give the required selectivity. Also as the intermediate frequency is lower than the actual received frequency greater selectivity can be obtained. A further advantage of having a fixed IF is that it allows the use of crystals in the filters. These give an exceedingly high degree of selectivity, but they cannot be made to be variable.

Superhet Circuitry
A block diagram of a fairly straightforward single conversion superhet is shown in Figure 6.4. It shows all the blocks which are required to make a basic receiver. Inevitably some of the more expensive receivers on the market today will be more complicated and possess more circuit blocks. Even so, the one shown will be fairly typical of a number of receivers and serves for the purpose of explanation.

On entering the receiver the signal passes straight into the first stage of RF tuning. Often this stage will employ some RF amplification to boost the signal level before the mixer. Whether there is any amplification or not the tuning is essential because it is required to reduce the "image response" to an acceptable level. This image is caused by the fact that there are two frequencies which can be received by any one combination of local oscillator and intermediate frequencies. Take as an example a receiver with an intermediate frequency of 455 KHz and a local oscillator of 1000 KHz. It is possible with this combination to receive signals on 1455 KHz as well as 555 KHz. As a result the RF tuning stage is required to allow only the wanted frequency through.

Once the signal leaves the RF stage it passes into the mixer where it is converted down to the intermediate frequency. Mixers can take many forms. Some receivers will utilise active ones which give gain, whilst others may use a passive one using diodes.

Also entering the mixer is the local oscillator. This is normally tuned using a variable capacitor. Usually this capacitor will have two or more sections or gangs so that the RF circuit can be tuned at the same rate as the oscillator. This approach has the advantage that only one control is required to tune the receiver.

The main requirement for the oscillator is that it must be stable. Whilst this may not be quite so important for the reception of AM or FM signals it is vitally important if the receiver is to be used for SSB or CW. This is because the pitch of the audio from the output of the receiver will vary by the same amount as the oscillator drifts, in the same way as it does in the direct conversion receiver.

Once the signals leave the mixer they pass into the IF amplifier. In this section the majority of the gain and selectivity for the receiver is provided. Usually there will be several stages of amplification, each coupled with tuned IF transformers to provide the selectivity. If very high degrees of selectivity are required then a crystal filter can be fitted. Normally these filters are only fitted in communications receivers because they are quite costly.

After the IF stages the signal is demodulated. This can be accomplished in one of a number of ways dependent upon the type of transmission in use.

If AM is required then it is usual to employ a diode detector which can be made up from just a few components. Generally the output from the last IF stage is passed into a diode to rectify the signal. Then a capacitor placed across the output is used to remove the radio frequency components leaving only the required audio signal. The circuit shown in Figure 2.5 is typical of what is usually used.

If FM is to be used then a number of different approaches can be used. Phase locked loop detectors are very popular especially for hi-fi systems, because they can easily produce very good results. Even so, more traditional designs using decreet components can still produce results which are more than acceptable.

Finally if single sideband or CW is to be used a beat frequency oscillator and product detector are needed. Together they provide a further stage of mixing to bring the signals down to audio frequencies.

Once detected the signals are amplified so that they can drive either a loudspeaker or headphones.

Double Conversion Superhets

As the frequency of operation is increased some problems with the basic single conversion superhet become more apparent. In order to overcome them it is possible to introduce another frequency conversion to give the double conversion superhet.

The most noticeable problem is that of the stability of the local oscillator. The fact that it has to operate up to fairly high frequencies, and that it has to be switched to cover the frequency range means that it can never be as stable as today's conditions demand. One solution which was very popular before the advent of frequency synthesisers was to use a switched crystal oscillator as the first oscillator. This is used to convert a band of frequencies, usually 500 KHz to a broad band first IF between 5.0 and 5.5 MHz. A variable local oscillator is then used to convert the signal down to the fixed IF which contains all the selectivity. Using this type of receiver the stability can be improved dramatically. This is because the first oscillator uses crystals and can be switched without the performance being noticeably impaired. The variable frequency oscillator can also be made very stable because it is not switched, it operates at a much lower frequency and it also covers a much smaller range.

Another problem which becomes more apparent at high frequencies is that of image rejection. As the frequency of reception becomes higher so the frequency difference between the image response and the required frequency becomes a much smaller percentage of the reception frequency. As a result of this it is not possible to achieve such high levels of image rejection. In order to illustrate this take the example of a communications receiver with a 455 KHz IF. When it is tuned to a frequency of 1 MHz, the image will be at 1.910 MHz. This is sufficiently far away to obtain good rejection. However, take the example when it is operating at 28 MHz. At this frequency the image will be at 28.910 MHz. As the percentage frequency difference is comparatively small the image response is likely to be a significant problem. The way to overcome this is to increase the intermediate frequency. In fact this has been done in the double conversion superhet in Figure 6.5. Having an IF of 5.0 to 5.5 MHz it means that the image frequency at 28 MHz will be at least 10 MHz away which will significantly improve the problem. It is also found that many receivers today will use an IF of 9 MHz reducing the problem still further.

The block diagram of the double conversion superhet is by no means the only type which can be used. Modern advances in technology have meant that many new ideas have been incorporated into many of today's receivers. Frequency synthesisers are one example. Also modern filter technology has allowed intermediate frequencies to rise without any sacrifice of selectivity. In fact frequencies of 10.7 MHz or 9 MHz for HF receivers are fairly common. In spite of this receivers will still usually employ two and sometimes three conversions, although they will not follow exactly the same block diagram as shown in Figure 6.5.

VHF/UHF Receivers
The descriptions of receivers so far have been primarily concerned with ones for use on the HF bands. Fortunately all the basic principles used for the HF receivers still apply at VHF, UHF and higher, although some minor differences are

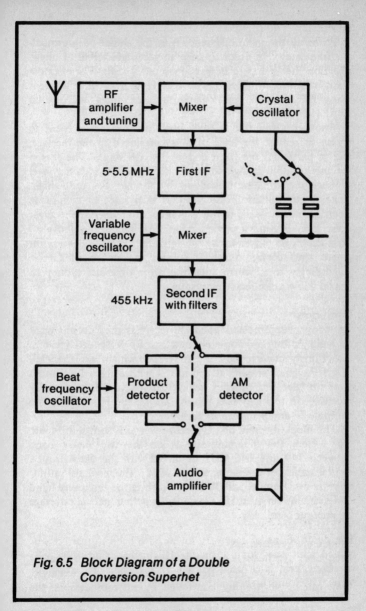

*Fig. 6.5 Block Diagram of a Double
Conversion Superhet*

inevitable.

Probably the main difference is in the choice of intermediate frequency. In order to keep an acceptable level of image rejection the IF has to be kept reasonably high. For example many receivers for 2 metres have an IF at 10.7 MHz whereas many HF receivers (particularly the older ones) will use an IF of 455 KHz.

Another difference is that much more effort is spent in trying to reduce the level of noise produced in the receiver, and in particular the front end or first RF stage. The reason for this is quite straightforward. On the HF bands the level of background noise picked up by the aerial is quite high. General atmospheric noise together with a lot of man-made electrical noise means that it is pointless to reduce the receiver noise level beyond a certain point. At frequencies above 30 MHz the noise picked up by the aerial falls and reaches a point where the receiver noise is by far the dominant factor. Accordingly it is worth spending some time and money to obtain a low noise receiving system.

Converters

As many people possess good HF receivers they do not want to build or buy a completely new one for VHF or UHF use. Accordingly many people use converters which take the VHF or UHF signal, amplify it and mix it with a fixed local oscillator to give a frequency which can be tuned by the HF receiver. In this way it is possible to use the HF receiver as a tuneable IF and utilise all its facilities.

The block diagram of a typical converter is shown in Figure 6.6. Here the incoming signals on the two metre band between 144 and 146 MHz are mixed with the signal from a crystal oscillator operating at 116 MHz. The resultant output appears between 28 and 30 MHz which is the ten metre band and available on most HF equipment whether general coverage or amateur band only.

Frequency Synthesisers

Frequency synthesisers are being used increasingly in amateur equipment because they offer many advantages. For example, they can be very easily controlled by microprocessors, the

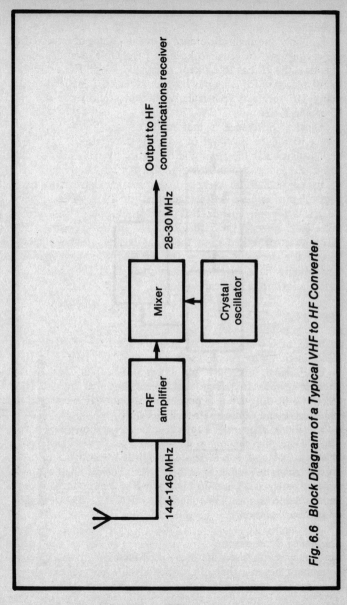

Fig. 6.6 Block Diagram of a Typical VHF to HF Converter

Antenna

144-146 MHz

RF amplifier

Mixer

Crystal oscillator

Output to HF communications receiver

28-30 MHz

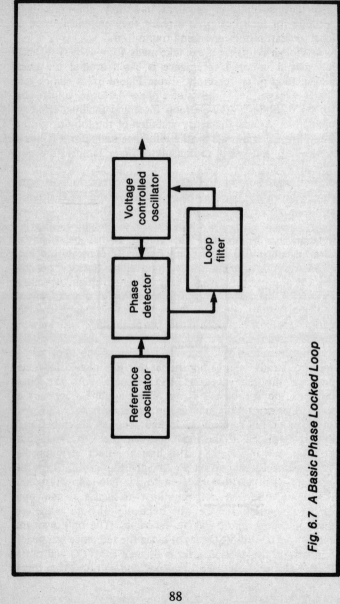

Fig. 6.7 A Basic Phase Locked Loop

frequency stability is excellent and they are exceedingly versatile for their cost. As a result they are widely used on local oscillators in receivers and transmitters.

Although synthesisers can take many forms, the type which has gained universal acceptance is based around the phase locked loop or pll for short. From Figure 6.7 it can be seen that the basic loop consists of a phase detector, voltage controlled oscillator (VCO), a loop filter and finally a reference oscillator. As the frequency stability of the loop or synthesiser is totally governed by the reference oscillator it is crystal controlled, and often contained within a temperature controlled oven.

The operation of the basic phase locked loop is fairly straightforward. The reference oscillator and VCO produce signals which enter the phase detector. The phase detector then produces an error signal as a result of the phase difference between the two signals. This voltage is then passed into a filter which serves several functions. It controls the loop stability, defines many of the loop characteristics and also reduces the effect of any sidebands which might be caused by any of the reference signals appearing at the VCO input.

Once through the filter the error voltage is applied to the control input of the VCO so that the phase difference between the VCO and reference is reduced.

When the loop has settled and is locked the error voltage will be steady and proportional to the phase difference between the reference and VCO signals. As the phase between the two signals is not changing, the frequency of the VCO is *exactly* the same as the reference.

In order to use a phase locked loop as a synthesiser a divider is placed in the loop between the VCO and phase detector, see Figure 6.8. This has the effect of raising the VCO signal in proportion to the division ratio. Take the example when the divider is set to 2. The loop will reduce the phase difference between the two signals at the input of the phase detector, i.e., the frequency of both at the two phase detector inputs will be the same. The only way this can be true is if the VCO runs at twice the reference frequency. Similarly if the division ratio is 3, then the VCO will run at three times the reference frequency and so on. From this it

89

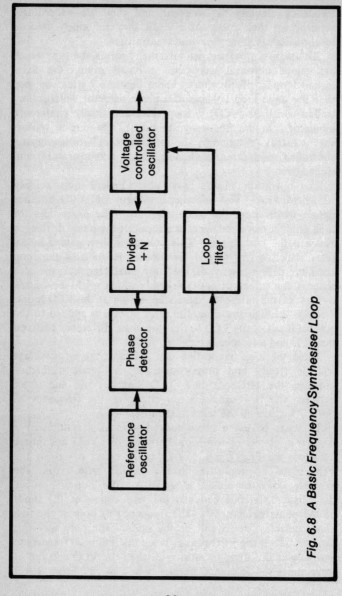

Fig. 6.8 A Basic Frequency Synthesiser Loop

90

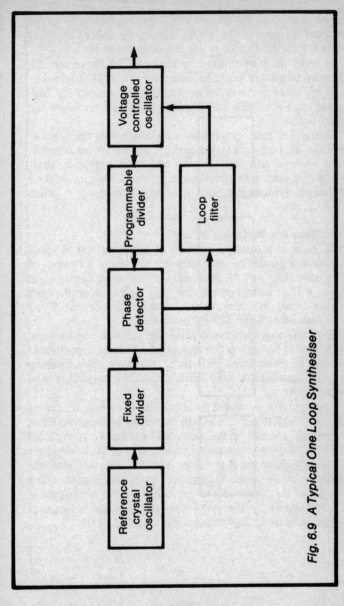

Fig. 6.9 A Typical One Loop Synthesiser

91

can be seen that the oscillator will step in multiples of the reference frequency. In fact by making the divider programmable the output frequency can be easily changed.

In order to have channel spacing of 25 KHz or less the reference frequency has to be made very low. This is generally done by running the reference oscillator at a relatively high frequency, e.g., 1 MHz and then dividing it down as shown in Figure 6.9.

This is the basic synthesiser loop which is at the heart of virtually all frequency synthesisers. It can be enhanced in many ways to give more flexible operation, step sizes which give almost continuous tuning and so forth. Despite all their advantages synthesisers have one major drawback — phase noise.

Phase Noise and Reciprocal Mixing
Phase noise is a form of noise which is present on all signal sources to a greater or lesser degree. Essentially it consists of noise spreading out on both sides of the main carrier as in Figure 6.10. Unfortunately the way in which synthesisers operate means that they produce much higher levels of this noise than other forms of local oscillator.

Phase does not always degrade the receiver performance. On a band with only a few signals of moderate strength it is unlikely to make much difference. However, when listening to weak signals on a band filled with strong stations it is of great importance.

The problem is caused by a process known as reciprocal mixing. Normally a station will mix with the local oscillator to produce a signal in the receiver IF passband. If the local oscillator frequency is changed slightly so that the station falls outside the passband it is still possible for it to mix with the oscillator phase noise to produce an inband signal. The strength of this signal will be dependent on the level of phase noise produced by the synthesiser and in some instances it may be sufficiently high to mask out a wanted signal.

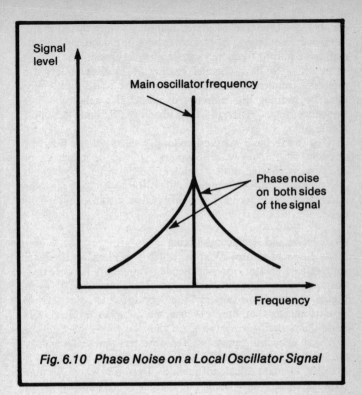

Fig. 6.10 Phase Noise on a Local Oscillator Signal

93

Chapter 7

TRANSMITTERS

Transmitters come in many different forms. Often they are combined with receivers to form a transceiver. This gives many advantages in terms of flexibility and ease of operation. As a result, transceivers are very popular, but it is still not unusual to hear of someone using a separate transmitter and receiver.

Transmitters also vary in the types of transmission that they can generate as well as in the frequencies they use. On the HF bands they generally cater for CW only or CW and SSB. On the VHF and UHF bands CW, SSB and FM are all widely used. Because of this it is not uncommon to find multimode transceivers which cater for all three modes. However, as FM is particularly popular many pieces of equipment cater for just this mode.

CW-Only Transmitters

CW transmitters are generally the simplest types to design or build. They require no circuitry for modulation save a simple means of turning the carrier on and off. In fact some of the very simplest designs contain as few as two or three transistors. Even so it is quite possible to make contacts over distances of a few hundred or a thousand miles. These simple transmitters are popular with home constructors because they can be built quite easily and the cost is relatively low.

The block diagram of a simple CW only transmitter is shown in Figure 7.1. Essentially it consists of an oscillator to generate the signal; one or more stages to amplify it to the required power level; a circuit to filter the signal and match the output to the aerial and finally a means of keying the transmission.

The oscillator is the heart of the transmitter. It needs to be stable and ideally it needs to be tuneable as well. The simplest and most reliable type is a crystal oscillator, like the one shown in Figure 7.2. It is ideal because it gives a fairly high output and does not drift to any noticeable extent. However,

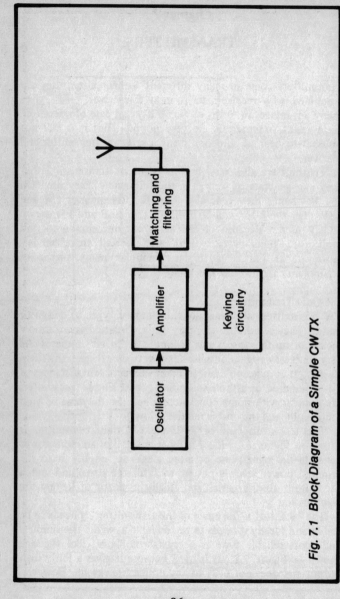

Fig. 7.1 Block Diagram of a Simple CW TX

96

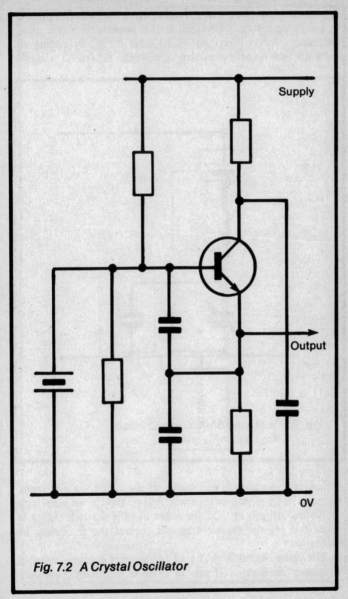

Fig. 7.2 A Crystal Oscillator

in its basic form frequency changes can only be accomplished by swapping crystals. Fortunately it is possible to obtain small frequency shifts, often up to 10 KHz or so, by adding an inductor and variable capacitor as shown in Figure 7.3. Careful

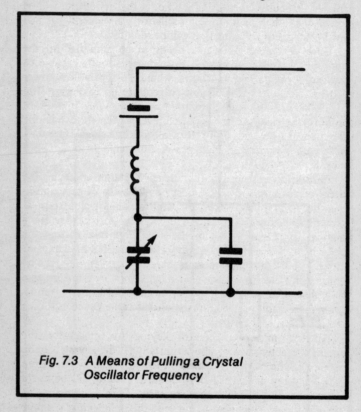

Fig. 7.3 A Means of Pulling a Crystal Oscillator Frequency

choice of the values is necessary. If the value of capacitance becomes too low the output will fall, or the circuit may stop oscillating altogether. On the other hand if the inductance is made too big the crystal may not control the frequency of oscillation.

The more desirable choice of oscillator is a proper variable frequency oscillator. If one of these is used then more care must be taken to ensure the oscillator is stable. This can be done by taking precautions like ensuring all the voltage rails are stable, choosing components with the correct temperature coefficient and making the unit mechanically robust. One further difficulty when using a v.f.o. is that its output will be lower than that of a crystal oscillator. As a result of this further stages of amplification will be required.

Once generated the signal needs to be amplified to the appropriate level. A typical crystal oscillator is capable of producing only a few milliwatts, whereas a typical low power (QRP) transmitter will be able to produce up to 5 watts and high power transmitters a hundred watts or more. In order to amplify the signal to the required level several stages may be required. In the case of a QRP transmitter a single stage may be necessary whilst a high power one will obviously need more.

In addition to amplifying the signal, a method of keying the signal is also required. The most obvious way of accomplishing this is to directly key the emitter circuit at a stage as shown in Figure 7.4. This is not always satisfactory for a number of reasons. One of the most important is that the stage being keyed may consume a few hundred milliamps or more. Whilst this may be acceptable if a straight key is to be used, many electronic or mechanical keyers may not be able to withstand this. To overcome the problem an extra transistor can be incorporated into the circuit to be keyed as shown in Figure 7.5.

Apart from the method of keying the transmitter, the keying characteristics are also important. If the keying is to be sharp, i.e., the carrier is turned on too fast as shown in Figure 7.6a then key clicks will be produced. These will be heard either side of the signal and can easily cause interference to other stations. In order to prevent this happening a simple filter can be added to the keying circuit. This function is carried out by C_1 in conjunction with R_1 and R_2 in Figure 7.5.

Although the amount of filtering or envelope shaping is not critical it can make the signal difficult to read at especially high speeds if it is taken to excess as shown in Figure 7.6b. An envelope similar to that shown in Figure 7.6c is about optimum.

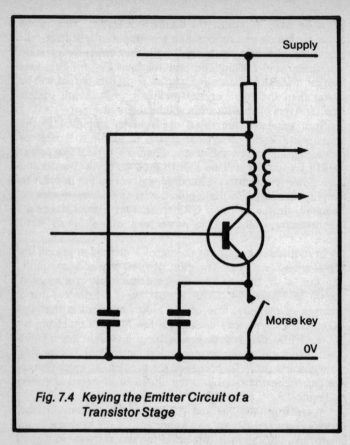

Fig. 7.4 Keying the Emitter Circuit of a Transistor Stage

The last stage in the transmitter through which the signal has to pass contains the matching and filtering. This is necessary to ensure that the optimum amount of signal reaches the aerial, and any spurious signals are reduced to reasonable levels.

The impedance matching is required because the maximum power transfer occurs when the source impedance (in this case the final amplifier output impedance) is the same as the load impedance (in this case the aerial impedance). Generally an impedance of 50 ohms is used as standard and all transmitter outputs and aerials are designed to match to this.

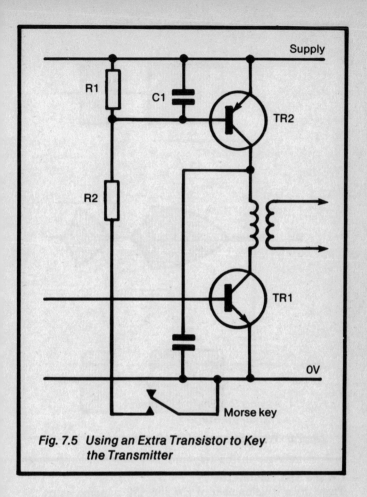

Fig. 7.5 Using an Extra Transistor to Key the Transmitter

Output filtering is most necessary as it prevents the radiation of any spurious signals which may cause interference to users on other frequencies. In a simple transmitter like that in Figure 7.1 the spurious signals will be as a result of the harmonics produced. A low pass filter such as that in Figure 7.7 is needed to remove them. It is usually found that five or seven elements are sufficient.

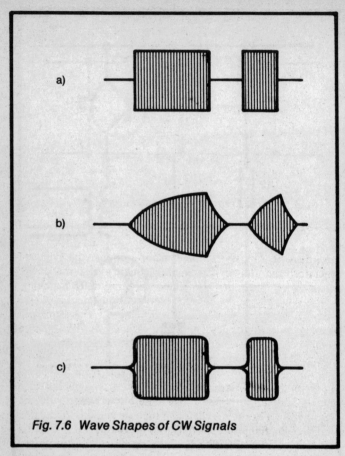

Fig. 7.6   Wave Shapes of CW Signals

CW and SSB Transmitters
There are a large number of CW and SSB transmitters on the air, either as transmitters in their own right or as part of a transceiver. By their very nature they are more complicated than the CW-only one just described. Even so if they are split down to their various blocks it is not too difficult to understand their operation.

A block diagram of a typical single sideband transmitter or the transmit path in a transceiver is shown in Figure 7.8.

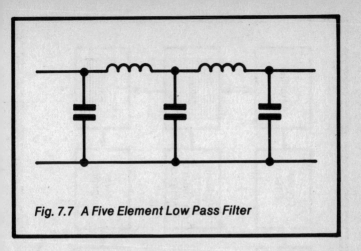

Fig. 7.7   A Five Element Low Pass Filter

Essentially it consists of three major sections: the sideband generator; the tuning and mixing circuitry and the power amplification with its associated filtering and matching.

The sideband generator is the section of the circuitry where the actual single sideband signal is developed. This signal will be at a fixed frequency, normally on one of the standard receiver intermediate frequencies, e.g., 455 KHz, 9 MHz, etc., and it will be at a fairly low level.

In the sideband generator the audio signal from the microphone enters an audio amplifier where it is amplified to a suitable level to enter the mixer. Here it is mixed with the output from a crystal oscillator so that the audio is modulated onto a radio frequency carrier. As a type of mixer called a balanced mixer is generally used the signal which is produced contains the upper and lower sidebands with the carrier reduced in level by 20 dB or so. This double sideband signal is filtered to remove the unwanted sideband and leave the single sideband signal. As a filter with a narrow passband and a sharp cutoff is required crystal filters are generally used.

The next stage of the transmitter is the tuning and mixing circuitry. In this section the signal is converted to its final frequency. This can be done in many ways using one or more conversion or mixing processes. Probably the most straight-

103

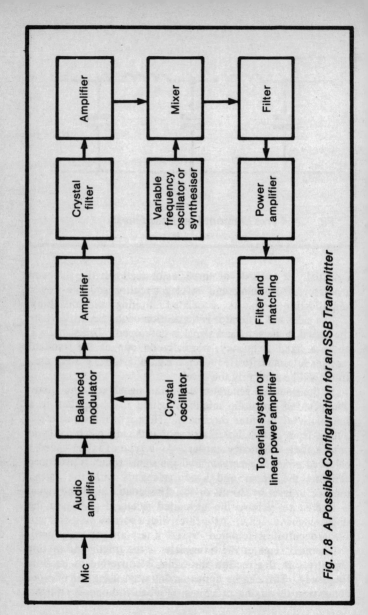

Fig. 7.8 A Possible Configuration for an SSB Transmitter

forward method is to use a single conversion and a frequency synthesiser to generate the local oscillator signal.

Once the signal has been converted to its final frequency it needs to be well filtered to prevent any of the unwanted mix products passing into the final amplifier.

The final amplifier will consist of several stages and will bring the signal up to the required power level. Many of today's HF transmitters and transceivers are capable of delivering up to 100 watts or more to the aerial. If still higher powers are needed then it is usual to have a separate linear amplifier.

In addition to amplifying the signal output filtering and matching is required as in the simple CW transmitter. It matches the output stage to the aerial and filters out any unwanted or spurious signals.

The transmitter as it stands can only be used for single sideband operation. However, it is quite easy to add a CW facility and this can be done in a number of ways. Probably the most obvious method is to use a keyed audio oscillator. A more popular method is to apply a voltage to the balanced modulator in the sideband generator. This has the effect of unbalancing the modulator and allowing the carrier through. If this method is used then the crystal oscillator frequency is generally shifted by a few hundred Hertz to place the carrier in the passband of the crystal filter. A few other minor considerations have to be taken into account. One of these is, of course, that the audio circuits have to be muted to prevent them generating any signals in the CW mode.

Narrowband FM Transmitters

Frequency modulation is very important as a mode of communication on the VHF and UHF bands where it is widely used for mobile, portable and other local communications. It can be generated in a number of different ways dependent upon the type of transmitter in use. For example, most of today's commercially made rigs will use synthesisers. In these units the modulation is generally applied directly into the synthesiser itself. For the home constructor one of the simpler methods of generating a VHF FM signal is to use a low frequency crystal oscillator with several frequency multiplier stages as shown in Figure 7.9.

In this example the crystal oscillator operates at 8 MHz, although it is possible to use 12, 18 or even 24 MHz. The oscillator is switched to enable several frequencies to be used. This is obviously an expensive way of achieving multichannel operation, but it is the most straightforward.

There are several different ways of applying frequency modulation to this stage. One method is to place a varicap diode across the crystal and apply the audio voltage to it to pull its frequency slightly. This is not very satisfactory because the differing crystal characteristics will change the level of modulation from one frequency to the next. It is also found not to be very linear and this results in distortion of the audio.

The most favoured way is to use a phase modulator such as that shown in Figure 7.10. This is far more satisfactory, but it does have a response characteristic which rises with increasing audio frequency. In order to overcome this an inverse characteristic is first applied to the audio by R_1 and C_1.

The level of modulation applied at this stage need only be fairly small. This is because the amount of deviation is multiplied by the same number that the signal frequency is multiplied by. So that in order to produce 3 KHz deviation (the accepted amount for narrowband FM) at 144 MHz, only 3/8 KHz need be applied at 8 MHz.

The phase modulator stage is followed by the multiplier stages each tuned to pass the wanted harmonic and reject the unwanted ones. Using multipliers it can be quite easy to select the wrong harmonic and obtain an output on the wrong frequency, or have high levels of spurious output signals. As a result these stages should be carefully tuned with the use of a dip meter or good absorption wavemeter.

Once the signal has been multiplied up to the correct frequency it can be amplified and filtered ready to be transmitted.

Speech Processing

One of the problems encountered when using a transmission to carry speech is the high dynamic range, or variation in level of a speech waveform. This is particularly important for single sideband transmission because the actual power transmitted is

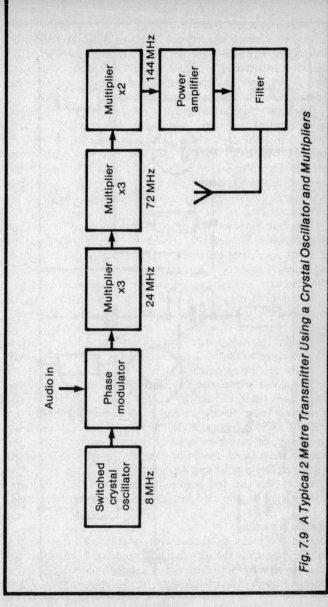

Fig. 7.9 A Typical 2 Metre Transmitter Using a Crystal Oscillator and Multipliers

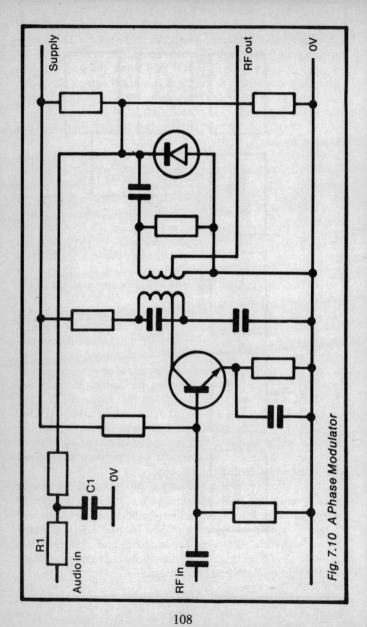

Fig. 7.10 A Phase Modulator

108

proportional to the level of the speech. As the transmitter will have to be able to handle the peaks in the speech, the average power transmitted will be much less than this. Typically the average power will be at least 12 dB below the peak. This is obviously not very efficient, and as a result speech processors are used to increase the average power level whilst keeping the peak the same. This has the effect of making the signal sound stronger and it is often possible to gain 6 dB or more in signal level purely by using a speech processor.

There are three main ways in which a speech signal can be processed. It can be compressed, clipped and the frequency response can be tailored.

The first method, compression, involves reducing the dynamic range of the signal. This is done by reducing the gain of an audio amplifier as the signal becomes louder. This can be done instantaneously so that individual waveform peaks are compressed. Alternatively it can be done by introducing a time constant into the circuitry which controls the gain. If this is done the system will tend to follow the envelope of the waveform.

The second type of processing is clipping. This is very similar to the instantaneous form of compression, and it involves clipping or removing any of the peaks of the waveform which exceed a certain level.

When either instantaneous compression or clipping is used a filter is needed to remove the harmonic distortion products which the process introduces. Generally a filter of this type would have a cutoff frequency of around 3 KHz. Even with this distortion products will remain within the wanted audio frequency range, and if the clipping is made too severe the distortion products will rise to a level where the signal becomes difficult to copy.

Apart from removing distortion products, filters can be used to tailor the audio response so that only the frequencies which contribute to the signal intelligibility are included. For a telephone line a bandwidth of 300 Hz to 3.3 KHz is found to be acceptable. However, for amateur communications it is possible to reduce this still further at the expense of removing some of the "naturalness" of the signal.

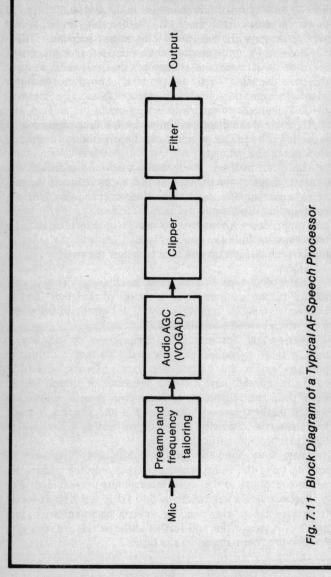

Fig. 7.11 Block Diagram of a Typical AF Speech Processor

In many of the speech processors which are on the market today all three types of processing are used. A typical "audio" processor is shown in Figure 7.11. The first stage is used as an input buffer stage and as a filter to limit the bandwidth. This is followed by a compressor or voice operated gain adjusting device (VOGAD). This stage removes the level variations in the speech signal. Then the signal is clipped and finally filtered to remove the unwanted distortion.

Whilst this type of processor is very useful the amount of clipping which can be used is limited by the distortion which can be tolerated. This problem can be overcome if a single sideband signal is generated and clipped. If this is done all the harmonic distortion will occur at multiples of the radio frequency and can be easily filtered out. Unfortunately these RF processors require more circuitry than their AF counterparts and are more expensive.

Chapter 8

AERIALS

The aerial is an important part of any amateur radio station. Upon it depends the whole performance of the station. Even though it is sometimes possible to use just an odd length of wire for receiving, results will be far better if a proper aerial is used. In fact the necessity for a good aerial is made even more apparent if it is to be used for transmitting. It is quite true to say that a poor aerial will mean that the whole station will give disappointing results despite the sophistication and expense of any equipment which may be connected to it.

Aerials come in many forms: some are centre fed, others are end fed; some may use a coaxial feeder whilst others can use open wire or balanced feeder; again some might have a single element whereas other designs may use several elements to make them highly directional.

With such a wide choice of aerials it is not always easy to decide which is the best type for a given situation. The necessity of having a good antenna often has to be balanced against its looks and the tolerance of family and neighbours. In order to overcome this many people use a lot of ingenuity when designing and erecting aerials. As a result it is necessary for any short wave listener or radio amateur to have at least a basic understanding of aerial theory.

Constituents of an Aerial

An aerial system is usually made up from three parts: the radiator; the matching and coupling circuitry; and the feeder which is used to connect the transmitter to the radiator.

The purpose of the radiator is self-explanatory as it serves to radiate the signal. The feeder is needed to connect a transmitter to the radiator as it may be located away from the radiating section of the aerial. One reason for this is that it is usually necessary to erect the aerial as high as possible or away from buildings or other obstructions to obtain the best results. In some instances long runs of feeder may be necessary to connect the transmitter to the radiator.

Matching and coupling arrangements are needed between the transmitter and the aerial to ensure the correct impedance match. This matching is required for a number of reasons. First of all it is found that the maximum amount of power can be delivered from the transmitter to the aerial if their impedances are matched. By placing an aerial tuning unit between the two matching can be achieved. A second reason is that many of today's modern transmitters will not operate satisfactorily if they are poorly matched. There is often a risk of damaging the output stage or it may sometimes be more prone to self-oscillation.

Feeders

Feeders or transmission lines are used to transfer RF energy from one point to another introducing only a minimal amount of loss. This is achieved by propagating an RF wave along the length of the feeder and allowing it not to radiate. They do this by containing the electric and magnetic fields associated with the wave to the vicinity of the feeder.

There are several forms of feeder. Probably the best known type is the coaxial feeder or "coax" for short. It consists of an inner conductor surrounded by an insulating dielectric and covered with an outer screen or braid. In turn there is a final insulation cover to act as protection. It carries current in both the inner and outer conductors, but because they are equal and opposite all the fields are confined to within the cable and cannot radiate. As there are no fields outside the cable nearby objects do not affect its properties and it is ideal for situations where it has to be run through a house.

Coax is termed an unbalanced cable. This is because its outer braid is generally earthed. As a result it can only directly feed a load which is similarly unbalanced, e.g., a vertical aerial loaded against earth. If it is required to feed a balanced load then an RF transformer known as a balun must be used to ensure the system operates correctly.

The second form of feeder is known as open wire or ribbon cable. It consists of two parallel lines or wires which are held apart by spacers or thin dielectric medium made up as part of the cable itself. For HF operation where this type of feeder is generally used, the spacing can be anywhere from about an inch up to six inches. The spacing is not critical provided that the characteristic impedance of the feeder does not have to be accurately known.

This type of feeder operates by carrying equal but opposite currents along each wire. As a result the fields cancel one another at a distance and the signal is confined to the vicinity of the feeder. Unfortunately nearby objects affect its performance and it is not suitable for long runs in houses. However, it does have other advantages over coax in that it can withstand bad mismatches and it is balanced.

A third type of feeder is known as a single wire feeder. This has to be arranged in such a fashion that there is a true travelling wave along it, and it does not radiate significantly. This cannot be achieved very easily, and then only with certain antennas like a Windom. Further inefficiencies result from earth return losses which still further reduce its effectiveness. As a result this type of feeder is very rarely used these days.

A final type of feeder is called waveguide. It consists of a solid metal conductor with a hollow rectangular or occasionally a circular centre. It is used only at microwave frequencies and is relatively expensive. Accordingly it is not often used in amateur projects.

Characteristic Impedance and Velocity Factor

It has already been mentioned that the maximum power transfer from a transmitter to an aerial occurs when the impedances are the same. Feeders themselves are found to have an impedance and this is of great importance when designing and erecting aerials.

The impedance of a feeder can best be demonstrated by taking the example of an infinitely long line with no losses. A signal applied to this line would propagate along it for ever and never be reflected or returned. As the energy propagating along the wire is always travelling and not stored the line would look like a pure resistor to the transmitter.

If the line was cut at a finite distance from the transmitter and the end left either open or short circuit then any signal travelling along the feeder would not be able to travel any further. In this case the only way for it to travel is to be reflected back the way it came. If then a variable resistor is connected to the end of the line some power will be dissipated in the load. As the value of the resistor is reduced it is found that more power is transferred to the load and less is reflected. Eventually a point is reached when all the power is dissipated in the resistor, and none is reflected. If the value of the resistor is reduced beyond this point less power is transferred to the resistor and more becomes reflected.

The value of the resistor when no power is reflected represents the impedance of the feeder itself and it is known as the characteristic impedance. Generally coaxial cables have an impedance of 75 ohms if they are to be used for domestic television, or 50 ohms if they are for professional or amateur radio use. Open wire feeders come in a variety of impedances, but 75 ohms, 300 ohms or 600 ohms are standard.

In all cases, it is possible to determine the characteristic impedance of a cable. For a coaxial cable it is governed by the ratio of the diameter of the inner conductor and the inner radius of the external braid. In the case of an open wire feeder it is the ratio of the wire diameter to the spacing. In addition to this it is found that the relative permittivity of the dielectric between or around the conductors also affects the impedance.

Not only does the permittivity affect the impedance but it also changes the rate at which the signal travels along the feeder. In fact the velocity is reduced by the square root of the relative permittivity. This difference in velocity is known as the velocity factor.

In many cases it can be as low as 0.66. In other words the signal travels along the cable at 0.66 times the speed of light. Whilst this may not appear to be particularly important it similarly affects the wavelength of the signal in the feeder. This can be particularly important when it is necessary to cut resonant lengths of feeder for use as matching stubs or the like.

Voltage and Current Waveforms
In any aerial the current and voltage distribution will vary according to the position in the aerial. Some points will carry

a high current and have little voltage whilst others possess a high potential but carry little current. Take a typical example the half wave aerial shown in Figure 8.1. From this it can be

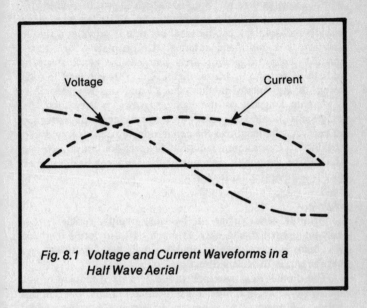

Fig. 8.1 Voltage and Current Waveforms in a
Half Wave Aerial

seen that the voltage reaches a maximum at either end and falls to zero in the middle. Conversely the current is at its maximum in the middle falling to zero at either end. From this it can be imagined that the feed impedance would vary according to the position where the antenna is fed. Near either end it would be very high, whilst at the centre it would be low. In actual fact it does not fall to zero but reaches a minimum.

Types of Aerial

There is an enormous variety of aerials which are available to the amateur. Each type has its own advantages or drawbacks. However, over the years a number of different types have become more popular as being suitable for the average person with the average garden.

Longwire

The term longwire has come to encompass a whole host of simple end fed wires. Generally they consist of a length of wire, as long as possible, erected as high as possible. This wire is then connected to the receiver via an ATU. For a receiving station this solution can be ideal because it provides a simple solution to a multiband antenna. Unfortunately for a transmitting station it is not ideal because the aerial starts to radiate as soon as it leaves the ATU. This can lead to high levels of RF energy in the "shack" and this is undesirable.

A true longwire as the name suggests, is very long. In practice it should be several wavelengths long at the frequency in use. As the length of the aerial in increased it is found that the lobes of maximum radiation or reception move closer to the axis of the aerial. Eventually the aerial can be considered as a true "end fire" antenna.

Dipole

The dipole aerial is one of the most popular aerials as it is easy to construct and easy to erect. It also forms the basis for many other types of aerial which are directional and exhibit a gain in certain directions.

The dipole, as shown in Figure 8.2, is often thought of as a half-wave aerial, and indeed it is most commonly found in this form. However, it can be any convenient number of half wavelengths long. As a half wave aerial it exhibits little gain or directivity as shown by its polar diagram in Figure 8.3(a). However, as the length is increased it develops pronounced lobes which progressively move towards the axis of the antenna as shown in Figure 8.3(b).

By looking at the voltage and current waveforms it can be seen that the dipole is fed at a point of high current and low voltage. This means that it has a low feed impedance. In free space the exact value of its feed impedance is 78 ohms, but in the average garden with the proximity of other objects, including the earth itself, this is altered and it is quite in order to use 50 ohm cable with a balun. Whilst it is always best to use a balun because this ensures the correct operation of the aerial it is sometimes acceptable to omit it and just connect the centre of the coax to one leg and the outer to the other. As an

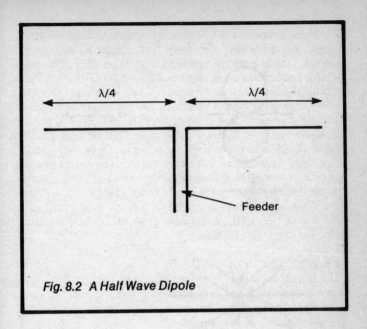

$\lambda/4$ $\lambda/4$

Feeder

Fig. 8.2 A Half Wave Dipole

alternative to using 50 ohm coax 75 ohm twin or ribbon feeder can be used.

The length of the aerial is quite critical especially if coaxial cable is to be used. The length is not exactly equal to a half wavelength in free space for a number of reasons. One is called the end effect. The result is that the actual length is shorter and it can be calculated reasonably accurately, at least in the HF bands by the formula:

$$\text{Length (feet)} = \frac{479}{f(\text{MHz})}$$

In practice it is best to cut the aerial slightly longer and then shorten it slightly once it has been assessed. By doing this the aerial can be cut to give the optimum performance for a particular portion of the band.

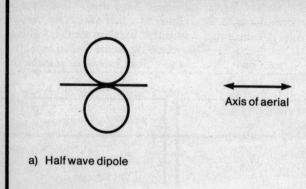

Axis of aerial

a) Half wave dipole

b) An example of an aerial longer than half a wavelength

Fig. 8.3 Polar Diagrams

The dipole is quite tolerant to being bent. One variant of the aerial which uses this characteristic is the inverted V dipole. As its name suggests it is in the form of an inverted letter V. This aerial works well because the portion of the aerial carrying the high current section is in the centre and this is where most of the radiation occurs. By keeping this portion as high as possible its performance can be improved.

It is not always convenient to erect separate aerials with separate feeders for each different band used. One way of overcoming this is to use a dipole as a half wave aerial on one band and as a three half wavelength aerial on another. This is possible on 7 and 21 MHz where the aerial is used as a half wave antenna on 7 MHz and as a three half wave antenna on 21 MHz.

Another approach is to use a single feeder to supply a number of different dipole elements as shown in Figure 8.4.

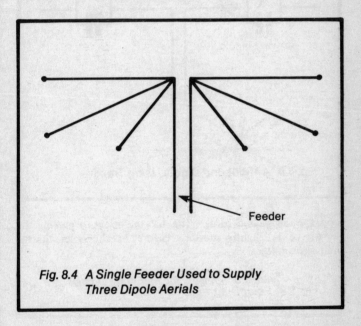

Fig. 8.4   A Single Feeder Used to Supply
Three Dipole Aerials

If this is done it is advisable to spread the elements as shown in the diagram to prevent them interacting too much.

A further idea is to use a trap. This is a parallel tuned circuit which will stop a particular band of frequencies passing through it. In the case of Figure 8.5 a dipole is cut to l_1 for a particular band. The trap will stop the frequencies for this band passing through, but will allow the frequencies for the band corresponding to l_2. In fact the trap acts as a loading

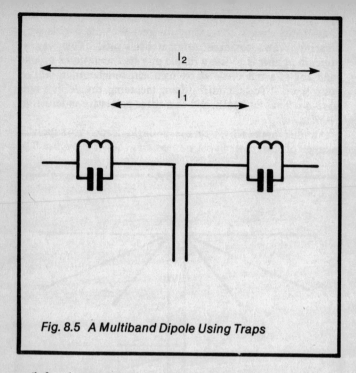

Fig. 8.5 A Multiband Dipole Using Traps

coil for the second band. This has the effect of making the length of l₂ slightly shorter. Figure 8.6 shows lengths for half wave dipoles.

Figure 8.6   Lengths for Half Wave Dipoles

Frequency (MHz)	Length (Feet)
1.8	266
3.5	137
7.0	68.5
10.0	47.5
14.0	34
18.068	26.5
21.0	23
24.89	19
28.0	17

The Doublet

This type of aerial is used comparatively infrequently, yet it offers the possibility of multiband operation with only a single aerial. The aerial operates by using an aerial tuning unit to bring the whole antenna system, including the feeder into resonance (see Figure 8.7). The main points to be aware of

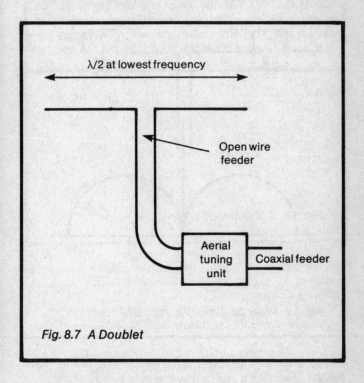

λ/2 at lowest frequency

Open wire feeder

Aerial tuning unit

Coaxial feeder

Fig. 8.7 A Doublet

when considering this type of aerial are that the aerial itself must be longer than half a wavelength at the lowest frequency of operation. In addition to this the 600 ohm line should preferably be longer than a wavelength. However, if the line is too long the system becomes very narrow band and the aerial tuning unit will have to be adjusted after only small changes in frequency. Finally the ATU must have a balanced output. Apart from these points this aerial is an ideal solution to many people's requirements for HF operation.

Verticals

The vertical is an aerial which has become popular with HF and VHF operators alike. It offers a low angle of radiation which is ideal for VHF use where any high angle radiation is lost because it cannot be reflected. Figure 8.8 illustrates a polar diagram. For HF operation as well it can be very useful where a low angle of radiation is required for DX operation.

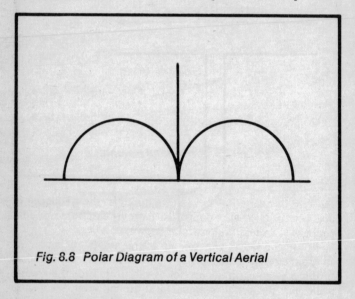

Fig. 8.8 Polar Diagram of a Vertical Aerial

The most popular length for a vertical is a quarter wavelength. It enables a good performance to be achieved without the aerial being too large. It is also possible to use other lengths such as a five-eighths wavelength which can give a better low angle performance. However, antennas using more than a quarter wavelength are more popular at VHF and UHF where size is not such a problem.

A vertical can be driven against a ground plane as shown in Figure 8.9. The radials used to form the ground plane are

124

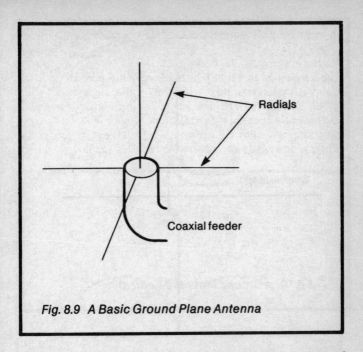

Radials

Coaxial feeder

Fig. 8.9   A Basic Ground Plane Antenna

generally a quarter of a wavelength long at the frequency of
operation. It is also normal to have at least three or four
equispaced around the vertical as shown.

At HF the radials can take up a large amount of space. As
an alternative it is possible to "ground mount" the antenna.
In this case an earth connection is substituted for the ground
plane and the aerial is mounted at ground level, see Figure
8.10. For this arrangement to operate satisfactorily the earth
must be good. Apart from ensuring that the DC conductivity
is good it is also possible to bury radials under the ground to
improve the RF performance. The advantage of a ground
mounted vertical is that it takes up very little space, however,
the disadvantage is that with the aerial being at ground level
it tends to be screened by nearby objects.

Yagi Array
In order to change the directional characteristics of a basic

125

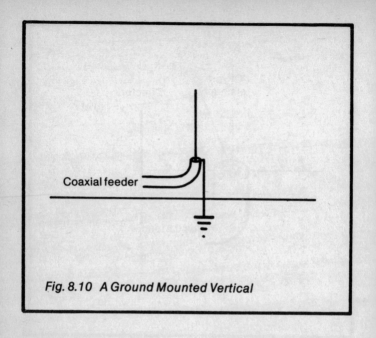

Fig. 8.10 A Ground Mounted Vertical

dipole it is possible to place other elements called parasitic elements close to it. The mutual coupling between the dipole or driven element and the parasitic ones means that power is either reflected or directed in a certain direction. An aerial like this using a dipole with a reflector and directors is known as a Yagi after a Japanese pioneer in the field.

It is found that if the driven element has another element about 5% longer placed near it then power will be reflected away from the parasitic element to reinforce the signal travelling away from the reflector. Similarly if an element about 5% shorter is used it will direct power away from the driven element towards it, reinforcing the signal in that direction. It is possible to use a reflector and one or more directors as shown in Figure 8.11, to give a highly directive aerial. Although it is possible to use several directors, it is found that the addition of further reflectors does not noticeably give any improvement.

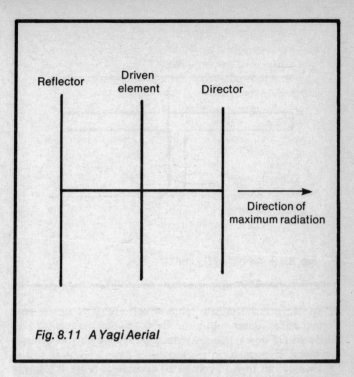

Reflector

Driven element

Director

Direction of maximum radiation

Fig. 8.11 A Yagi Aerial

The addition of parasitic elements causes the feed impedance of the dipole or driven element to fall drastically. In
order to overcome this an arrangement known as a folded
dipole is used, see Figure 8.12. By using this the aerial
impedance is quadrupled enabling standard coax to be used
again.

This type of aerial is sometimes used on the HF bands.
However, it is on the higher bands where it finds its main uses.
Most amateur stations active on the VHF or UHF bands will
use one, but by far and away it is used most of all for UHF
broadcast TV reception.

Some Practical Aspects
The effectiveness and safety of an aerial can be improved by
the way in which it is erected. Precautions taken when fixing

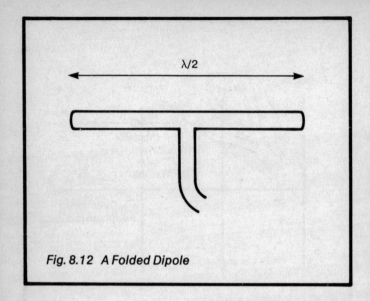

$\lambda/2$

Fig. 8.12 A Folded Dipole

it up can make it radiate more effectively or retain its performance for longer. Additionally a well-erected aerial is less likely to fall down, thereby reducing the possibility of damage or injury.

One of the first aspects to be considered when erecting a wire aerial is the points or places where it can be attached. One suitable anchor is a convenient place on the house. Another could be a convenient tree. Whilst a tree is often ideal, consideration must be given to the movement of the tree in the wind. The arrangement shown in Figure 8.13 is the standard way to overcome the problem, being simple and yet quite effective.

When deciding upon the weight, consideration must be given to the amount of tension required. This is particularly important because ordinary types of copper wire, whether PVC covered or not can stretch quite considerably. Sometimes this may not be particularly important, but in the case of an aerial like a dipole which has to be cut to exactly the right length, it can be quite annoying. As a general rule the tension should be just enough to stop any undue sag. Obviously larger

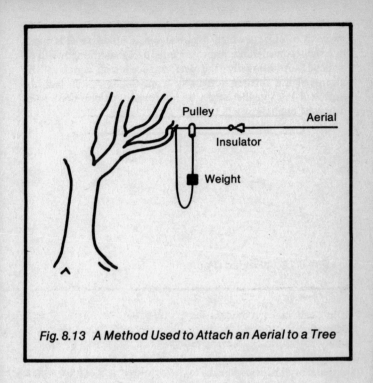

Fig. 8.13 A Method Used to Attach an Aerial to a Tree

aerials for the low frequency bands will need more tension and this may still cause a problem. In cases like these hard drawn copper wire can be used. Normally amateur radio dealers will be able to give details of suppliers.

An important point to note when using coax feeder is to ensure that any ends which are outside must be sealed to prevent moisture entering the cable. If this is not done water can pass down the dielectric between the centre conductors and the braid. This can drastically increase the loss of the feeder, rendering it useless. To prevent this a proper sealant such as silicone rubber should be used and even then it should be inspected at intervals to make sure the sealant is still intact. PVC or similar tapes should not be used as they do not seal well and they do not last for long.

Finally, an aerial should be erected as high as possible and away from objects which might screen it. If an aerial is raised in height considerable improvements in signal strength will be noticed. Additionally, the performance of an aerial will be improved the further it is away from buildings. In fact not only will the signal strength be improved, but also noise from domestic appliances will be less.

Chapter 9

GETTING STARTED

It can often seem quite difficult for the beginner to get started. Decisions about the best type of receiver, the optimum aerial and even where to put all the equipment are not always as easy to make as they may seem at first sight. They are also important, as a station which is well planned from the very beginning will be more enjoyable to use and it will enable the most to be obtained from the hobby and the equipment.

In order to start off on the right footing there are a number of steps which can be taken. A good start is to enlist the help of a local and willing radio amateur or short wave listener. This is probably best done by joining a local radio club. In fact there are quite a number of them dotted around the country so it should not be too difficult to find one which is within easy travelling distance.

Another approach is to subscribe to one of the amateur radio magazines. There are several of them which are published these days so it is possible to pick the one which suits best. These magazines cover a wide range of topics from constructional articles, reviews of equipment, to general articles about various aspects of the hobby, news of what is going on and so forth. Some of them even have a club section. This can be very helpful when trying to find a local club.

It is also worth while joining the national radio society. In the United Kingdom it is the Radio Society of Great Britain or RSGB for short. In the U.S.A. it is the American Radio Relay League or ARRL. Both of these societies provide many functions for the radio amateur. They publish a monthly magazine, operate a QSL bureau for delivering QSL cards in bulk, issue awards, run contests, negotiate for the radio amateur over licensing matters with the relevant governing departments and perform many other functions.

Buying a Receiver
One of the first hurdles to be overcome when setting up a station is obviously buying the receiver. As this can be a

fairly major investment it is worth looking into what is really wanted, what is likely to be available and what price can be paid.

There are several considerations to be made when deciding upon what sort of receiver is wanted. Firstly it is necessary to look at what type is wanted. For most people some form of communications receiver is the best choice. This will make a good basis on which to build up the station. It will give coverage of the HF bands, and if necessary a converter can be used with it to listen to a band in the VHF or UHF spectrum. However, other people may only want to listen to the VHF and UHF bands and in this case it may be that a scanner could be a better choice.

Even if a communications type of receiver is chosen it is worth looking at the coverage this will give. Most of them will cover between 1.5 MHz and 30 MHz, but some will tune down to a few hundred kilohertz. Alternatively an amateur bands only receiver might be considered. These receivers have the advantage that they give better bandspread on the amateur bands than a general coverage one, but at the expense of covering only the amateur bands. This can be rather restricting at times, but may be a good option if only amateur operation is required. Today very few amateur band only receivers are made because new techniques used these days enable good bandspread to be achieved over all the frequencies covered.

The price will be another major consideration, and this is likely to determine whether a new or second-hand receiver is bought. Whilst it is nice to buy new the price can often make this impractical. Fortunately there are many second-hand receivers available at much less cost. In particular, some of the older valve receivers can be bought quite cheaply and represent very good value for money. There can be certain drawbacks to this approach. Older receivers will be larger, heavier and the maintenance aspect will have to be considered. This is especially true for valve receivers, as the valves are becoming more difficult and expensive to obtain and very few dealers will service them.

A choice of where to buy the receiver also needs to be made if a second-hand receiver is bought. There is always an element of risk if it is being bought privately from a reader's advertisement in a magazine or elsewhere. However, this is probably the cheapest route and there are some good bargains to be taken. A sale through a dealer will be much safer as there will be a guarantee and after sales service. Unfortunately it will cost more as the dealer has overheads and then there is often sales tax to be paid. Probably the ideal solution is to buy a reliable receiver from a friend, but it rarely happens that a friend is selling the right receiver at the right time.

The Aerial
The choice of aerial is very important for both listening and transmitting stations. Although the basic outlines about aerials have already been given in Chapter 8 a few practical hints are given here.

For a listening station it is possible to use almost any piece of wire around the house just to pick up some signals. However, it will be quickly found that this sort of approach is inadequate. The signal strength of the stations will be poor. In addition to this there will be a lot of electrical noise picked up from items like televisions, home computers, vacuum cleaners and so forth. This noise will often mask out the weak DX stations which are being sought.

Probably the best all-round solution for an HF short wave listening station is a longwire with an ATU as shown in Figure 9.1. If it is made fairly long, erected as high as possible and kept away from the house as much as possible then it should perform well.

For a transmitting station the position is a little different. Longwires will radiate RF energy as soon as they leave the ATU. This can lead to high levels of RF in the vicinity of the equipment which can lead to RF feedback into the equipment, not to mention the increased risk of interference to domestic televisions, hi-fi's and radios if the shack is in the house. High levels of RF are also unwise from a health point of view. Generally there is no problem with low powers or non-directive aerials, but if high powers or directive aerials are used there may be a risk. In view of this it is best to keep RF away from the house.

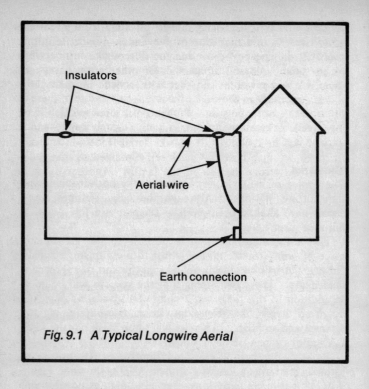

Fig. 9.1 A Typical Longwire Aerial

Generally for the transmitting station aerials such as dipole verticals and the like are better. They can be erected away from the house and are likely to cause less problems.

Radio Room

Whilst it is possible to put a receiver in the living room and listen to it there, almost invariably extra ancillary units are required. The station is likely to grow even further if a transmitting licence is obtained, so at the outset it is worth setting aside a suitable area or room for the radios. Often the term radio "shack" is used for this and amateurs will frequently be heard talking about the shack. This is probably a very apt term considering the state in which some of them are.

Whilst it is ideal to be able to set aside a room for the shack this is usually not possible and a number of other alternatives have to be considered. Places like lofts, garden sheds, cupboards and all manner of other areas have been successfully converted. In fact with a little ingenuity it is surprising what can be done.

When choosing where to put the shack a few points should be noted. Obviously it should have a mains supply and it should not be too difficult to take aerial feeders in and out. It is also good to have the shack self-contained so that it can be shut off from the rest of the family. Another point to consider is the temperature. Places like lofts and garden sheds can suffer from wide variations in temperature which can make operating much less pleasant in the height of summer or in the middle of winter.

Operating Table

Having selected a location for the shack the next stage is to install a table for the equipment. In some cases it may be possible to press an existing table into service or even buy one. However, it will usually be necessary to build one.

The table, whether it is bought, built, or an existing one, should be fairly strong. Many old valve units are very heavy and even the weight of modern equipment can mount up surprisingly quickly as new units are added. With this in mind it is best to err on the safe side and have a table that is too strong rather than one which is rather suspect.

The size of the table is also important. The accepted height of the work-top on most desks is about 30 inches and this is quite comfortable to work at if a chair is used. The width should be sufficient to accommodate all the equipment, and if possible it is worth adding a little extra space for future additions of equipment. Finally, the depth — this should be enough to allow for about 15 inches in front of the equipment for log books, morse keys, microphones, constructional projects and everything else. Any less space and it becomes cramped.

If possible a shelf can be installed above the table. This can be used for smaller ancillary units like aerial tuning units, standing wave ratio meters, loudspeakers and so forth.

It is also a good idea to install mains distribution blocks of sockets. As the amount of equipment increases the mains wiring can very quickly become a tangle of wires. By using distribution blocks sufficient sockets can be installed so that no multiway adaptors are used, however do not exceed the maximum power limit of the point.

The wiring from these distribution blocks can be taken back to a single switch. This can be used to turn the whole station off without having to remember to turn off each individual item. A further precaution would be to include a residual current circuit breaker. This detects an inbalance of current between the live and neutral lines. If it exceeds a certain amount it will trip and turn the mains off. As an inbalance like this can be caused by a short to earth or even someone touching the live line it can be a very wise safety precaution. It should be noted, however, that it will not prevent people getting shocks or damage from shorts, it will only mean that the chance of serious injury or damage is reduced.

Equipment Layout

Once the table is built and installed to one's satisfaction it should not be forgotten that the actual layout of the equipment on it can also contribute to the ease of operating the station. Although many ideas can be incorporated into the layout, ones similar to that shown in Figure 9.2 have been found to be quite successful.

The main receiver or transceiver should be placed centrally on the table with its tuning dial a couple of inches above the table top. This means that one's arm can rest on the table whilst tuning the receiver, saving a lot of arm ache during extended periods of operation. A second receiver or transceiver should then be placed to the right of this so that when it is being used one does not have to reach across from right to left to operate it. A linear amplifier or a transmitter (if a separate transmitter and receiver are used) can be placed to the left of the main transceiver. It is then best to keep the microphone to the left-hand side so that it can be held in the left hand whilst taking down notes with the right hand. Also if a morse key or keyer is used it should be towards the right of the table where it can be reached easily.

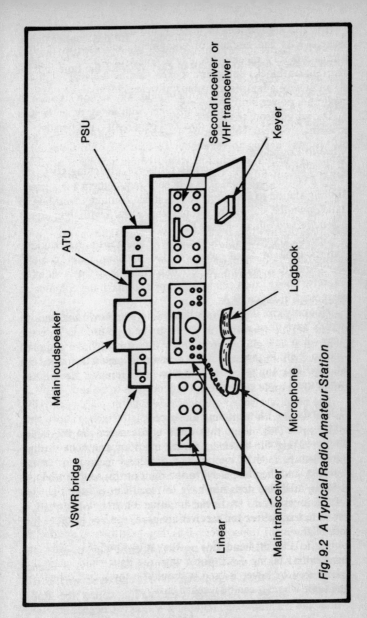

Fig. 9.2 A Typical Radio Amateur Station

PSU

Second receiver or VHF transceiver

Keyer

ATU

Main loudspeaker

Logbook

VSWR bridge

Microphone

Linear

Main transceiver

137

If a shelf is available this can be used for the smaller items. In fact it is particularly useful for items like VSWR bridges because they need to be kept in easy view all the time in case any antenna faults occur.

This is obviously only a broad guide. Any station layout will depend on what is available together with many other factors include whether it is to be operated by a right-hand person.

Station Logbook

It is helpful and often quite interesting for a listening station to keep a station logbook. It is a licence requirement for a transmitting station to keep one. In fact it can be quite rewarding to note down the stations which have been heard with their signal strengths and other relevant facts.

Special logbooks for both receiving and transmitting stations can be bought from many of the amateur radio dealers. However, it is quite easy to make one up from a suitable exercise book. Lines can be ruled in it to make the columns as suggested in Figure 9.3.

Not only can the logbook be used to note down the stations which have been received, but it can also be used to note the date when new aerials were erected, new equipment acquired and so forth. In this way it can be used to keep a history of the station. Keeping a logbook is also good training for the day when the licence comes and a logbook has to be kept.

Towards the Transmitting Licence

After some time listening on the bands many people decide they would like to obtain a transmitting licence and talk to other radio amateurs over the air. The first stage is to find out the requirements because they vary from one country to another. Usually a theory test needs to be passed to obtain a licence which gives access to the bands above 30MHz. Additionally a more test is needed for the traditional short wave bands below 30MHz.

In the U.K. there are four types of licence. First there are the standard Class A and Class B licences. The Class B licence gives access to the bands above 30MHz and to obtain this it is necessary to pass a theory examination called the Radio Amateurs Examination. To obtain a Class A licence it is also

Date	Time	Frequency (MHz)	Station heard	Signal report	Mode	QSL Sent	Recd	Comments

Fig. 9.3 A Suitable Receiving Station Logbook

necessary to pass a morse test. This entails sending and receiving at 12 words a minute.

Two Novice licences are also available. These are intended for newcomers to the hobby and accordingly the requirements for obtaining them are less. Although they allow the use of lower powers and restricted frequency ranges they still give sufficient facilities to enable many interesting contacts to be made. To obtain one of these licences a short course must be attended. This gives a good grounding in basic radio technology allowing more to be gained from the licence when it is obtained. Having completed this an examination has to be passed. Once this passed a Class B Novice licence can be obtained, and this gives access to the frequencies above 30MHz. If a morse test of 5 words a minute sending and receiving is passed, a Class A Novice licence can be obtained, giving access to all the novice bands.

To find out more about obtaining a licence the national radio society can be contacted. In the U.K. this is the Radio Society of Great Britain (RSGB), whilst in the U.S.A. the national society of the American Radio Relay League (ARRL). The addresses for both these organisations is given in Appendix 1.

It is usually the theory examination which will be tackled first. Generally it will require a knowledge of the licence conditions, operating procedures and radio theory. Preparation for it can take many forms. Initially a basic understanding and feel for radio theory can be gained by building projects, reading magazines and books on the subject and generally taking an interest in the subject. Knowledge about operating techniques can be gained by listening on the bands. However, when actually studying for the examination it helps to devote more time in direct preparation. Often special courses are arranged at night school. They are often worth attending because a well planned course will start right at the basic level and cover the whole syllabus. This should ensure that there are no gaps in anyone's understanding.

In addition to any courses there are often books specially written for people taking the exam. In the U.K. the RSGB publishes a very good preparation book called the RAE Manual. Equivalent books are published by the ARRL and are available in the U.S.A.

Learning the Morse Code

The morse test can often seem more daunting. However, many people have surprised themselves by settling down to learn the code and finding it much easier than they thought.

The first step is to be determined to have a good try at passing the test. Some people suggest setting a timescale, possibly even booking the test itself sometime ahead so that there is a goal to aim it. Another helpful idea is to learn with a friend. This helps because it keeps the momentum going much better. It also makes it more difficult to give up and there will be a sense of letting the friend down. However, the major necessity is to set aside a small amount of time each day. Fifteen minutes to half an hour is ideal, and remember, it is much better to do fifteen minutes EACH day rather than two hours or more one day a week.

When starting to learn the code it must be remembered that each letter must be recognised by its sound or rhythm. In fact it is of little use looking at a table of the morse code and learning the letter A as "dot dash" because this is not the way in which it is heard. One way of learning the code is to listen to the same letter being sent several times and then trying to associate the letter with the sound. Another way is to try to associate the rhythm of a letter with a phrase of common sound. For example, the letter F (. . – .) has the same rhythm as the phrase "did it hurt y' " or Q (– – . –) has the same rhythm as "God Save the Queen". Then the letter H (. . . .) has the same rhythm as the "clickety clack" of a railway coach travelling along the line. In this way a start can be made on learning some of the letters.

Having learned the alphabet and numbers it is necessary to start to practice reading the code. This can be done in a number of ways. Morse records and tapes come in useful here, as do electronic morse "tutors" and slow morse transmissions like those organised by the RSGB. Some good practice can also be gained by listening on the air. Bands like eighty metres and two metres are best because the speed of the morse is reasonably slow. With sufficient practice one's reading speed and accuracy will slowly increase. Then eventually it will come up to and above the standard required for the test.

Sending morse should never be contemplated un til it is

141

possible to read the code. This is because it is all too easy to develop bad sending habits if it is not possible to read morse. In fact it is a good idea in any case to tape-record some of one's own sending and listen to it later for bad sending. In this way any bad habits can be corrected as they creep in.

After the test has been passed there is no need to forget all about CW. A lot of time and effort will have been spent in learning it and it seems a shame that so many people let it lapse without really giving it a try. Often people are surprised how rewarding and enjoyable morse can be.

Appendix 1

ADDRESSES

American Radio Relay League

225 Main Street
Newington
Connecticut
CT 06111-1494
U.S.A.

Telephone:	860-594-0200
Fax:	860-594-0259
E-mail:	CompuServe:
	70007,3373@Compuserver.com
	America On line: hq@arrl.org

Radio Society of Great Britain

Lambda House
Cranborne Road
Potters Bar
Hertfordshire EN6 3JE
England

Telephone:	01707 659015

Index

Notes

Please note following is a list of other titles that are available in our range of Radio, Electronics and Computer books.

These should be available from all good Booksellers, Radio Component Dealers and Mail Order Companies.

However, should you experience difficulty in obtaining any title in your area, then please write directly to the Publisher enclosing payment to cover the cost of the book plus adequate postage.

If you would like a complete catalogue of our entire range of Radio, Electronics and Computer Books then please send a Stamped Addressed Envelope to:

BERNARD BABANI (publishing) LTD
THE GRAMPIANS
SHEPHERDS BUSH ROAD
LONDON W6 7NF
ENGLAND